P9-DJL-588

Armenia

A RUGGED LAND, AN ENDURING PEOPLE

BY LUCINE KASBARIAN

DILLON PRESS
PARSIPPANY, NEW JERSEY

To all Armenians who have sacrificed their lives
to defend their nation, faith, and heritage

Acknowledgments
I wish to thank my parents, Garabed and Aghavni Kasbarian, who taught me to value integrity above all; my brother, Antranig Kasbarian, who taught me to lead by example; and my uncles, the late Ardashes and Nishan Hamparian, who taught me to equip myself with books and knowledge.

I am also indebted to many others who supported this endeavor and kindly offered me access to archives or supplied me with photographs and illustrations at no charge to help defray production costs.

Grateful acknowledgment is made to the William Saroyan Foundation of San Francisco, CA, for permission to reprint an excerpt from "Inhale, Exhale" by William Saroyan.

Finally, I wish to thank my cousin, Anahid Hamparian, for bringing this project to my attention and my editor, Debbie Biber, for keeping me in line.

Photo Credits
Front cover: *l., m.* Garo Lachinian; *r.* Kevork Djansezian

Armenian International Magazine (AIM): 77, 146. Courtesy of the Armenian Library and Museum of America, Inc., Watertown, MA: 39. Ardem Aslanian: 46, 129, 131, 144. Lindy Avakian: 64. Arné Balassanian: 160. John Boloian: 13. Corbis-Bettmann: 124. Kevork Djansezian: 41. Editions Erebouni/State Gallery of Armenia, *Queen Shamiran with the corpse of Ara the Handsome* by Vardges Sureniants, 1899: 83. Armineh Johannes: 19. Antranig Kasbarian: 95, 107, 119. Lucine Kasbarian: 72, 99, 112, 115. Mkhitar Khatchatrian: 70. Ara Kopooshian/*The Battle of Avarayr* by Krikor Khanjian: 56–57. Harry L. Koundakjian: 93. Garo Lachinian: 8, 15, 26, 30, 96, 148. Ruben Mangasarian: 75, 122. Haig Najarian: 21. Eric Panosian: 91. (Halebian 1-83) Project SAVE: 62; (Lucile Sarkissian 1-91) Project SAVE, photo by Ray D. Lillibridge, courtesy of Lucile Gochigian Sarkissian: 136. Beth Rustigian-Broussalian: 36, 101. Courtesy, Alex Sarkissian: 140. Silver Burdett Ginn: 5, 45, 52. Chigita Tsuki: 127. Map by Ortelius Design (Pre-Soviet Armenian boundaries specified from the Treaty of Sevres, 1920): 6. Illustration by Arné Balassanian: 81. Illustration by Nishan Hamparian: 31, 55.

Library of Congress Cataloging-in-Publication Data
Kasbarian, Lucine.
Armenia : a rugged land, an enduring people / by Lucine Kasbarian. —1st ed.
p. cm. — (Discovering our heritage)
Includes bibliographical references (p.) and index.
Summary: An introduction to the geography, history, people, government, and culture of Armenia with emphasis on the challenges facing this newly independent nation.
ISBN 0-382-39458-5 (LSB)
1. Armenia (Republic)—Juvenile literature. [1. Armenia. (Republic)] I. Title. II. Series.
DS165.K37 1998
909' .0491992—dc21 96-47530

Cover and book design by Michelle Farinella

Published by Dillon Press
A Division of Simon & Schuster
299 Jefferson Road, Parsippany, NJ 07054

First edition

Printed in the United States of America

10 9 8 7 6 5 4 3 2 1

Contents

Fast Facts About Armenia

Official Name: Republic of Armenia (*Hayasdani Hanrapetutiun*)

Capital: Yerevan

Location: Armenia is situated between Europe and Asia in a region known as the Near East or Transcaucasus. To the north of Armenia is Georgia; to the east and southwest, Azerbaijan; to the east, the autonomous region of Nagorno Karabagh; to the south, Iran; and to the west, Turkey.

Area: About as large as the state of Maryland, Armenia is 11,490 square miles (29,800 square kilometers).

Elevation: *Highest*—Mount Aragats, 14,535 feet (4,430 meters) above sea level; *Lowest*—Araks River valley, 1,247 feet (380 meters) above sea level.

Population: *Estimated 1996 population*—3.7 million; *Distribution*—68 percent live in urban areas; 32 percent live in rural areas; about 96 percent are ethnic Armenians; the rest are Russians, Kurds, and other minorities.

Form of Government: Armenia declared its independence from the Union of Soviet Socialist Republics (USSR) on September 21, 1991, and became an independent state on September 23, 1991. It is an independent presidential republic with executive, legislative, and judicial branches.

Important Products: Minerals, grains, livestock, fruit, brandy, mineral water, *tuf* stone, chemicals, synthetic

rubber, and electronic equipment; chief trading partners include Georgia, Iran, Kazakhstan, Russia, and Ukraine.

Basic Unit of Money: Dram, introduced in November 1993 to replace the Russian ruble.

Official Language: Armenian; Russian is also spoken.

Major Religion: Christian; 94 percent of Armenians belong to the Armenian Apostolic Church.

Flag: Horizontal tricolor—red on top, blue in the middle, and orange on the bottom; the color red represents the blood that was shed over centuries under foreign rule, blue represents the sky, and orange represents the ripened wheat fields across the countryside.

National Anthem: “Our Fatherland” *(Mer Hairenik)*

Major Holidays: New Year’s Day—January 1; Christmas Day—January 6; Saints Vardanantz Day—February; Mother’s Day—April; Easter; Armenian Genocide Memorial Day—April 24; First Armenian Independence Day—May 28; Second Armenian Independence Day—September 21; Earthquake Victims Remembrance Day—December 7.

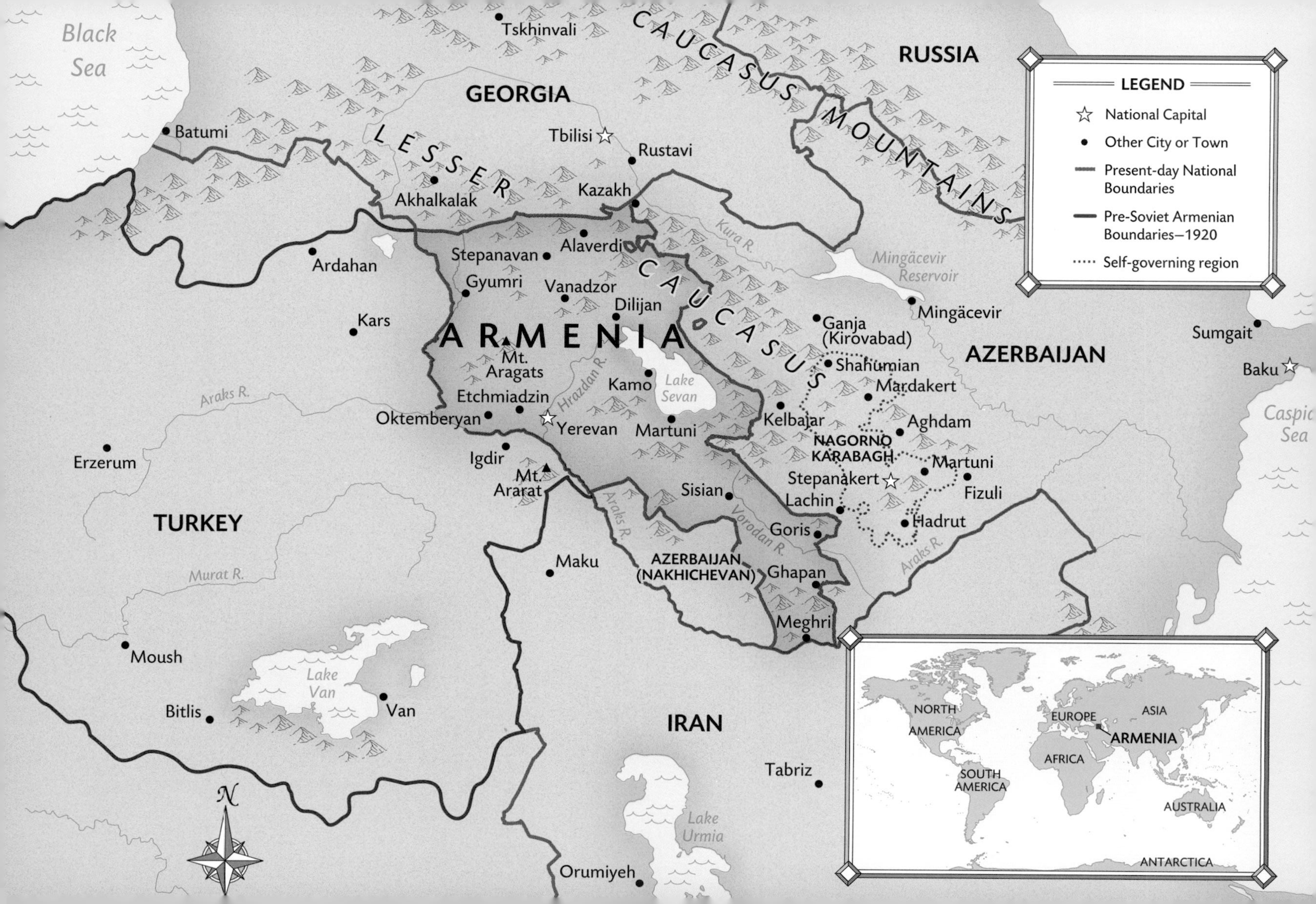
LEGEND
National Capital
Other City or Town
Present-day National Boundaries
Pre-Soviet Armenian Boundaries—1920
Self-governing region
RUSSIA
GEORGIA
ARMENIA
AZERBAIJAN
TURKEY
IRAN
AZERBAIJAN (NAKHICHEVAN)
NAGORNO KARABAGH
CAUCASUS MOUNTAINS
LESSER CAUCASUS
Black Sea
Caspic Sea
Mingäcevir Reservoir
Lake Sevan
Lake Van
Lake Urmia
Kura R.
Araks R.
Murat R.
Hrazdan R.
Vorodan R.
Batumi
Tskhinvali
Tbilisi
Rustavi
Akhalkalak
Kazakh
Ardahan
Alaverdi
Stepanavan
Gyumri
Vanadzor
Dilijan
Kars
Mt. Aragats
Kamo
Etchmiadzin
Oktemberyan
Yerevan
Martuni
Erzerum
Igdir
Mt. Ararat
Maku
Sisian
Goris
Ghapan
Meghri
Kelbajar
Ganja (Kirovabad)
Shahumian
Mardakert
Aghdam
Martuni
Stepanakert
Lachin
Hadrut
Fizuli
Mingäcevir
Sumgait
Baku
Moush
Bitlis
Van
Tabriz
Orumiyeh
N
NORTH AMERICA
SOUTH AMERICA
EUROPE
ASIA
AFRICA
ARMENIA
AUSTRALIA
ANTARCTICA

An Ancient Land and People

If asked to define Armenia, historians today would likely call it an ancient civilization, a very mountainous land, or a country of proud people who have been shaped by their rich but tragic history. Armenia, or Hayasdan as it is known to Armenians, is considered by many scholars and scientists to be the "cradle of civilization," the place where human society was born. In fact, the Bible suggests that Armenia is where the repopulation of the earth began. According to the Old Testament, after the Great Flood, Noah's ark came to rest on the mountains of Ararat. Modern-day findings support this account. One of the oldest artifacts in Armenia, safeguarded in the Etchmiadzin Museum, is a piece of wood believed to have come from Noah's ark. Mountain climbers and scientists continue to search for the remains of the ark on Mount Ararat, which is located today within the borders of the country of Turkey.

In this century, researchers uncovered other artifacts from ancient metal refineries in Armenia. Their findings showed that the Armenians inherited a civilization even older than that of the Egyptians. The Armenian people can be traced to the sixth century B.C., when written records first mention them by name. These early writings, known

as the Behistun inscriptions, tell the story of Darius, a powerful Persian emperor who commanded his warriors to conquer the Armenians because they had failed to obey him. The action of the Persians would be repeated by many other invaders over the centuries. Because Armenia was located between the world's Eastern and Western civilizations, it was a constant battlefield and a prize for conquering empires.

Where Is Armenia?

Positioned at the crossroads of Europe and Asia, historic Armenia—that is, the lands whose native peoples have in the past been Armenian—is located in Asia Minor, or Anatolia, and the Transcaucasus. Anatolia is the landmass that links the easternmost part of Europe with the westernmost part of Asia. Transcaucasus is the region of the Caucasus mountain range in the present-day countries of Armenia, Azerbaijan, and Georgia.

Today Armenia's neighbors are the countries of Georgia to the north, Azerbaijan to the east and southwest, Iran to the south, Turkey to the west, and the autonomous region of Nagorno Karabagh to the east. Historic Armenia includes lands in the region of eastern Anatolia, in present-day Turkey; Nagorno Karabagh and Nakhichevan, in present-day Azerbaijan; and Alkhalkalak, in present-day

Mount Ararat: the symbol of Armenia's origins

Georgia. As a result of foreign invasions and occupations, Armenia today is a fraction of its former size. In fact, it is the smallest of the 15 former Soviet Socialist republics.

Features of the Land

Although it is only about the size of the state of Maryland, Armenia gives the impression of being much larger. Mountain chains rise across the countryside alongside canyons, valleys, alpine streams, and extinct volcanoes. Armenia's sharply curving roads and winding hills make it impossible to travel in a straight line for very long. Even though Armenia is only 11,490 square miles (29,800 square kilometers) in size, it takes more than just a few hours to travel from one part of the country to another. The mountains of Armenia are the cause of this, although few Armenians would recognize them as handicaps. Many Armenians refer to the mountains as guardians of the people who live on the land. Armenian writers and others have paid tribute to these rulers of the skies. According to a popular saying, the mountains are as steadfast as the Armenians themselves and are a symbol of the people's attachment to the land. The tallest mountain in Armenia today is Mount Aragats. Its summit is more than 2 1/2 miles, or 14,535 feet (4,430 meters), above sea level and is covered with snow for most of the year.

Armenia's panoramic and colorful landscape varies, depending on the season, climate, time of day, and part of the country you are in. There are bustling towns dotted with street-corner stalls selling newspapers and souvenirs. Then there is wide-open backcountry interrupted only by tottering sheep heading off to pastures. Besides mountain bluffs and deep ravines, there are flatter regions, including valleys, foothills, and plateaus, where urban and rural settlements are located. Armenia is divided into eleven provinces: Aragatsotn, Ararat, Armavir, Gegharkunik, Kotaik, Lori, Shirak, Siunik, Tavush, Vayots Tzor, and Yerevan. Soil and plant life vary greatly throughout the countryside, which produces over 3,000 different plant species.

Most of Armenia's landscape is steppe, or mountain grassland, and rocky, dry environments. Armenians often repeat the rhyme *Hayasdan, karasdan,* which means "Armenia, the land of rocks." Because Armenia is so rocky, only 38 percent of the land is suitable for people to live on. Those parts of the country are densely populated, and the farmland there is used to its fullest extent. About 11 percent of Armenia is forest land, with many kinds of hardy trees, including oak, beech, and pine. Many of these areas are official nature preserves. The national forests are home to a wide variety of wildlife. There are more than 470 species of wild animals in Armenia, including mammals, birds, reptiles, and fish. Common animals such as boars, deer, foxes, and squirrels roam the woods of Armenia, as do more exotic creatures, such as lynxes, jackals, lizards, and porcupines.

Natural Sources of Water

Armenia is a landlocked nation, but it is not without water, for it has more than 100 mountain lakes. Although the unique composition of the earth's surface makes Armenia prone to earthquakes, it has also produced natural wonders such as waterfalls and hot springs. Many rivers flow near Armenia's roads, trenches, and cliffs. The Hrazdan, Vorodan, and Araks rivers are used to produce electricity and are partly redirected to irrigate areas that have no natural source of water. These rivers flow very rapidly, making them unsuitable for boating. Sevan, Armenia's largest lake, however, is popular among all kinds of water lovers. A year-round vacation resort, Lake Sevan is a good place for swimming, sailing, and other recreational activities. The lake is also famous for the delicious freshwater trout called *ishkhanatzook,* or prince fish. The fish got its name from the spots on its head that form the shape of a crown. Lake Sevan is also one of the largest hydroelectric sources in Armenia. Over years of excessive use, however, Lake Sevan's fish supply and water level have been depleted. Today the government of Armenia

Sailing on Lake Sevan

realizes that it must find an effective way to replenish the lake's nutrients and restore ecological balance.

A Dry Climate

The climate in Armenia also varies depending on where you are. The rise and fall in elevation throughout the country affects the wind and temperature and other atmospheric conditions. Armenia is at the same latitude as Spain, but because its mountains block moist air, Armenia's climate is much drier and warmer than Spain's. Armenia is generally dry all year round, with only about 8 to 31 inches (20 to 80 centimeters) of rain or snow annually. Extreme temperatures as high as 100° F (38°C) in the summer and as low as -22° F (-30° C) in the winter have been recorded in some areas.

A heavy veil of smog frequently hangs over Armenia's large cities. This air pollution develops from car fumes and exhausts from chemical-processing plants and factories. Mountains surrounding the cities do not allow the air to circulate freely in the valleys in which the cities are located. In the mountain regions themselves, the air is noticeably cooler and cleaner, and clear enough that you can see thousands of stars glistening at night.

Resources and Industry

About 1.2 million acres (486,000 hectares) of Armenia are arable, or suitable for cultivating fruit, vegetables, and grain. The most fertile area in Armenia is the Araks River Valley, just west of Yerevan. A wide variety of fruit, including cantaloupes, cherries, peaches, pears, plums, watermelons, and wine grapes, is grown there. Some of the more exotic fruits grown in Armenia are apricots, figs, mulberries, pomegranates, and quinces. Many Armenians believe that the apricot first grew in their land. This has never been proven, although the fruit's scientific name—Prunus armeniaca—suggests that the apricot may actually have originated there. Armenia's most important agricultural products include cotton, grains, grapes, sugar beets, potatoes,

A farmer collecting kindling wood

and tobacco. Armenia is also a producer of essential oils from plants such as geranium, rose, and peppermint, as well as specialty teas.

Although fresh water can be scarce, Armenia is a major producer of mineral water, or *jermuk,* with more than 700 natural deposits countrywide. There are several underground hot springs in Armenia. Most of the springs are in the Jermuk, Dilijan, Hankavan, and Vanadzor regions. A favorite spot is located in the southern region of Goris. To get there, travelers must make an exciting journey along swerving mountain roads. Underneath a place known as Devil's Bridge, there is a hidden natural mineral pool. In this secluded spot visitors can enjoy a scenic and luxurious mineral bath that bubbles like soda water.

Mineral resources found in Armenia include bauxite, copper, gold, silver, and other precious metals. Armenia also has large deposits of granite, lead, limestone, zinc, marble, volcanic pumice, and tuf stone. Driving along the main highways leading to Lake Sevan, travelers will notice black mountains of stone that sparkle in the sunlight. This stunning sight is created by tiny fragments of a shiny volcanic rock called obsidian. Thousands of years ago some mountains of Armenia were active volcanoes that spit out melted rock or lava. When the earth cooled, the lava hardened and broke up into little pieces of obsidian, which is now a gemstone.

Armenia's key industries are machine-tool construction, chemical and synthetic rubber manufacturing, metal cutting, and the production of knitwear, hosiery, silks, and shoes. Armenia also produces high-tech electronic equipment, such as computers, calculators, and lasers. Before it became an independent republic, Armenia produced trucks, tires, and about 25 percent of all Soviet elevators.

With no water gateway to the outside world, Armenia has to rely on its neighbors to allow products such as oil, gas, and electricity to pass through their borders. Some of Armenia's neighbors are not willing to allow such shipping. Since 1989 the countries of Azerbaijan and Turkey have cut off transportation of essential goods and humanitarian aid to Armenia because of a territorial dispute. Although this blockade has damaged economic growth and hampered the small republic's ability to maintain normal production levels and prosper on its own, Armenians believe that with time and diplomacy the embargoes will be lifted.

Cities and Other Sights

For centuries the majority of Armenians lived in the mountain highlands and tended animals. Today 68 percent of Armenia's population lives in urban areas. More than one million people, over one fourth of the country's population, reside in Yerevan, Armenia's most developed and cosmopolitan area and its capital.

Once a favorite tourist destination within the USSR, Yerevan is Armenia's cultural center and the thirteenth capital that Armenia has had in its long history. Yerevan boasts many historic landmarks and museums, universities and institutions, and theaters and restaurants. It even has a subway with chandeliers.

The city bridges ancient and modern times in both its architecture and its design. The elaborate etchings on the fronts of many buildings in Yerevan are testimony to the centuries-old Armenian tradition of stone carving. Bronze and stone statues of Armenian saints and heroes stand in public parks all over the city. Ornamented fountains, large and small, decorate almost every intersection. Old men play heated games of backgammon as they always have in the city's parks and gardens. Homes, breweries, and even martial arts clubs are nestled in the hills, valleys, and flatlands that make up the capital city.

Republic Square is one of the most interesting places in Yerevan, as many important structures are located there. The Hotel Armenia is the place where most tourists stay when they visit the country. There is always something happening at the hotel's restaurants and jazz clubs, cafes and wine cellars, meeting rooms and gift shops. If you want to hear the latest international news or find out who is in town, Hotel Armenia is the place to go. Across from the hotel are the "singing fountains" of Armenia. On summer

An aerial view of Yerevan

evenings, hundreds of people gather to watch the colored light shows that bounce off the cascades of water, and listen to music that seems to rise from the fountains themselves.

Built in 1929, the Government House building is just to the left of the fountains. Behind the fountains is a building that contains the Armenian Historical Museum, and the National Gallery of Armenia. The museum has more than 160,000 exhibits, which show how Armenians lived from the Stone Age to the beginning of the twentieth century. The National Gallery of Armenia is home to one of the broadest art collections in the former USSR.

Republic Square is also the location of government ministry offices. Near the center of the square is an empty pedestal on which Vladimir Lenin's statue once stood. Lenin was the leading force behind the Russian Revolution of 1917 and the first chairman of the Soviet Union. When the Armenian people voted for their national independence in 1991, Lenin's statue was removed, and the name Lenin Square was changed to Republic Square. For years, statues of Lenin and other Soviet leaders were prominently placed on busy streets and city parks throughout the USSR. When the Soviet Union collapsed, these statues were either knocked down or removed. Many have found new homes in museums and even scrap yards, where they stand or lie as reminders of an era that is now part of the past.

Also in Yerevan is one of Armenia's national treasures,

The Matenadaran

the Matenadaran. The Matenadaran is a library and storehouse for more than 13,000 ancient Armenian books and manuscripts. At its main entrance is an enormous statue of Mesrob Mashdots, the creator of the Armenian alphabet. Statues of pioneering historians, scientists, philosophers, and artists in Armenian history stand like guardians along the front arches of the building. Inside the library, scholars study documents, and specialists restore ancient manuscripts. In addition to housing works of ancient Greek philosophers such as Plato and Aristotle, the Matenadaran also possesses many ancient Greek works that have survived only in their Armenian translations. The translations are so faithful to the original languages in style that it has been possible to retranslate them into the original Greek with much precision.

The oldest church in Armenia lies just 12.5 miles (20 kilometers) outside Yerevan. Etchmiadzin Cathedral was constructed in the fourth century. Legend has it that Jesus Christ came down from the heavens to point to the site where the first Armenian church should be built. Translated, *Etchmiadzin* means "where the only begotten son descended." The district of Etchmiadzin is the Vatican City of Armenia. The Armenian *catholicos,* or pope, resides there. The current church complex houses the catholicos's residence, the cathedral, a seminary, a museum, outdoor gardens, and many monuments. The Etchmiadzin Museum exhibits ancient manuscripts, tapestries, jeweled icons, and other treasures.

Just 16 miles (25 kilometers) from Etchmiadzin lies Sardarapat, one of the most famous monuments in Armenia. Sardarapat was built to pay tribute to the Armenians who fought off the Turkish armies that invaded Armenia in 1918. The site features a huge bell tower whose bells are rung every year in memory of the victorious battle. Two enormous stone bulls with wings stand on either side of the monument as the protectors of Armenia, and the grounds are decorated with sculptures of poised eagles and stallions surrounded by flames.

Gyumri, Armenia's second largest city, is a cosmopolitan center with residential neighborhoods, art and music conservatories, and textile factories. Along the wide, tree-lined boulevards are monuments honoring Armenian war heroes as well as the remains of buildings destroyed in the 1988 earthquake, which according to some estimates claimed over 100,000 lives in the region. Visitors to Gyumri will see old women pacing the streets selling a sweet treat called *basdegh,* made of walnuts covered with honey and molasses. In warm weather, locals chat over ice cream at outdoor neighborhood cafes. At the marketplace, groups of men wave American dollar bills and Russian rubles in exchange for Armenian currency. Market vendors set out all kinds of items, including coffee urns, tank tops and gym shorts, and colored-glass pendants that ward off the "evil eye." This charm is called an *achk.*

Gyumri also has many beautiful but sorrow-filled cemeteries. Granite tombstones with photographic etchings cover hillsides all over the city. These unique gravestones are permanent reminders of the earthquake that was one of many tragic episodes in Armenian history. Cemeteries in Armenia often have picnic tables and chairs beside gravestones. It is a custom to continue honoring people long after they die. Families often visit cemeteries on special occasions to break bread with the spirit of their departed loved ones.

Vanadzor, Armenia's third largest city, is about 50 miles (80 kilometers) east of Gyumri. It is another industrial hub of the country. Metal plants and textile factories—some functioning, some dismantled—dot the landscape. Vanadzor is also studded with fruit trees. It is common to see young girls strolling arm in arm along the wide, breezy avenues. The center of town is crowded with municipal offices, high-rise apartment buildings, auto-mechanic sheds, and outdoor farmers' markets. On a typical day in the center of town, peddlers arrange their wares on street corners they share with men selling gasoline from tank trucks.

The cities of Yerevan, Gyumri, and Vanadzor are always humming with activity, but they are in dire need of modernization. Years of Soviet mismanagement are partly to blame, but overall, technical operations in Armenia are outdated and in a state of disrepair. Many factors have stunted Armenia's economic growth, including the ongoing blockade, limited resources, the lack of financing since the breakup of the USSR, and the damage done to local industries by the 1988 earthquake. Because of shortages all water and electrical currents flow for only brief intervals each day, and gas and oil for heating are also commonly in short supply. Industry in Armenia has slowed because raw materials are not available or have been seized at the borders before they can enter the country. As a result, it has been difficult to maintain public services such as buses, telephones, garbage collection, and sewage systems across the nation.

Country Life

Of Armenia's approximately 3.7 million inhabitants, about 32 percent live in rural areas. Most are farmers. In the past, country folk worked on farms that were government owned. Today those farms are owned and operated by groups of families. Other pastures have been broken up into portions and distributed to individual families. Rather than live on their farm property, many farmers still live in village homes and walk or drive to the vineyards, orchards, or pastures that belong to them.

Rural life is physically demanding. People organize their lives around their crops and livestock. Farmers might work in tobacco fields, grow sunflowers, or run apiaries—collections of beehives. A day in the country is a long one that usually begins before the sun rises. Cows are milked, and steers are herded out to graze, all before dawn. Depending on the season, farmers may be busy fertilizing soil and planting seeds or gathering their hay and produce. Normally farmers store their harvest for use in the winter or sell it at the nearest market.

Armenian village homes are made primarily of wood or stone, and there is usually a lot of space between houses.

A shepherd with one of his flock

Many households have their own vegetable gardens for growing food. On warm, sunny days families air out their colorful carpets and mattresses on roofs and verandas. Where plumbing is not available, outhouses are common substitutes for indoor bathrooms.

In the wintertime many remote mountain villages are snowbound. Winter is a time for indoor activities. Many homes have wood-burning furnaces. Animals are sheltered in stables, and families often eat fruits and vegetables that were preserved during the summer months. Unless there is a village clinic or transportation to a city hospital, people who need medical treatment during the winter often have to rely on home remedies and midwives—women trained to help other women give birth.

While some villagers own cars, most rely on bicycles, horses, or a local bus to travel to the nearest city. Yet even today some people are known to live their entire lives without traveling outside their own villages, just as their ancestors did hundreds of years before them.

A New Government

Armenia is a presidential republic. The president serves for five years and is commander in chief of the country. According to law, he selects the vice president, prime minister, and other advisors. The prime minister presides over a council of ministers. Each is in charge of a specific government department, such as agriculture, education, energy, health, and interior affairs. The Armenian lawmaking body is the Parliament, also known as the National Assembly. Parliament members are called deputies and are elected by local districts throughout the country. Parliamentary elections are held every four years. The judicial system of Armenia is made up of district courts and a supreme court.

Armenia is struggling to develop its democratic government, and some observers have noted that there is much work to be done. Independent human rights groups such as Amnesty International have pointed out that political parties are officially allowed to express their views freely, but groups that oppose the current regime have been subjected to many pressures and restrictions. International observers from the Organization for Security and Cooperation in Europe (OSCE) have reported on the need to reform governmental operations so that presidential elections can be freely and fairly run.

For decades the people of the Soviet Union learned how to "get around" ineffective laws and to deal with government controls and prohibitions. Today it is not always easy for Armenians and other national groups that were once part of the Soviet Union to believe in and obey new laws and develop a trusting attitude toward authorities—new or old. It will take time for Armenians of all ages to become self-sufficient, revive their national character, and observe democratic principles. But despite this uphill struggle, many Armenians are determined to survive and prosper.

NATIONAL CHARACTER AND CULTURE

A deep devotion to their faith and language has helped Armenians preserve their identity over centuries of invasion and occupation. In a way, the ancient Armenian church and the Armenian alphabet have been identity cards for the Armenian people. Ever since A.D. 301, when Armenia became the first nation to adopt Christianity as its state religion, Armenians have looked to the church to preserve their national character and to provide education and leadership. The church is firmly rooted in Armenian culture, and even in the land itself.

The entire church complex of Geghard Monastery, for example, is actually part of the land. This thirteenth century natural and human-made wonder, complete with dark passageways and caves, is carved out of the face of a mountain. Many churches and dwellings were built in this way to protect the Armenians from invaders. While the artistic beauty of such churches makes them national monuments, they are not just places to attend mass. Built on some of the most dramatic cliffs and in some of the most scenic spots in Armenia, church grounds and ancient cave dwellings are also considered the best locations for picnics and celebrations.

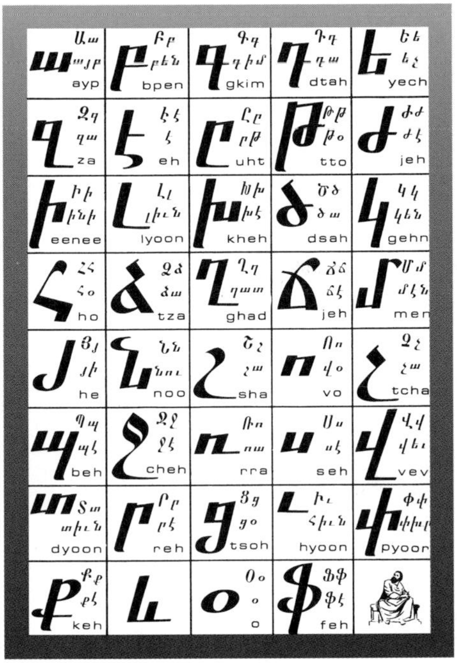

Ա ա ayp	Բ բ bpen	Գ գ gkim	Դ դ dtah	Ե ե yech
Զ զ za	Է է eh	Ը ը uht	Թ թ tto	Ժ ժ jeh
Ի ի eenee	Լ լ lyoon	Խ խ kheh	Ծ ծ dsah	Կ կ gehn
Հ հ ho	Ձ ձ tza	Ղ ղ ghad	Ճ ճ jeh	Մ մ men
Յ յ he	Ն ն noo	Շ շ sha	Ո ո vo	Չ չ tcha
Պ պ beh	Ջ ջ cheh	Ռ ռ rra	Ս ս seh	Վ վ vev
Տ տ dyoon	Ր ր reh	Ց ց tsoh	Ւ ւ hyoon	Փ փ pyoor
Ք ք keh	և	Օ օ o	Ֆ ֆ feh	

The Armenian alphabet

The Armenian language, the other key to the Armenian national identity, was spoken long before the Armenian alphabet was created in A.D. 406. There are three forms of the Armenian language. Classical Armenian, or *Grapar,* is the oldest form. Although extensively used in ancient times, today Grapar is used only in church rituals. Armenians today speak one of two similar forms of the language. Eastern Armenian, which was influenced by the Persians and Russians, is spoken in present-day Armenia, Georgia, Russia, and Iran. Western Armenian, which was influenced by the Romans, Greeks, and Turks, is spoken by the descendants of Armenians who once lived in areas now part of countries such as Turkey and Syria.

One unique aspect of Armenian churches is their unusual design.

What Are Armenians Like?

About 96 percent of all people in Armenia are ethnic Armenians. The remaining people are Assyrians, Azeris, Greeks, Jews, Kurds, Russians, Ukrainians, and Yezidis. An additional 4 million Armenians reside outside of the republic in what is called the Armenian diaspora. The diaspora includes all Armenians who were exiled or who emigrated from their homeland and settled in other parts of the world.

History has trained Armenians to adapt quickly to new and difficult surroundings and situations. Errands such as getting gas or buying groceries are not nearly as easy in Armenia as they are in some other parts of the world. Armenians are resourceful, or inventive. For instance, they might know how to brew coffee without a coffee pot or gas stove, chill foods without electric refrigeration, or juggle three jobs to make ends meet.

Armenians enjoy good company and conversation and will go to any length to make guests feel comfortable. Armenians value the family, arts and literature, and children most of all. Whether going out to dinner or just to the market, Armenians take pride in their appearance and dress their best. After having been cut off from Western countries such as the United States for so long, Armenian young people today love wearing jeans, T-shirts, and baseball caps with American emblems on them. They enjoy having their pictures taken, chewing bubble gum, and drinking Coca-Cola.

Armenians are said to be industrious. They are known to be ambitious in business and have particularly excelled as builders and architects, craftspeople, bankers, physicians, and lawyers. During the Soviet period, however, many factors changed how people all over the USSR felt about the benefits and rewards of hard work. For years there was a restrictive cultural atmosphere, salaries were low, and people had no say about how businesses in which they worked so hard were run. These conditions discouraged many people from being productive. Even in the face of new economic opportunities today, such attitudes have been hard to shake.

What's in a Name?

You can spot Armenians anywhere in the world by their last names. Almost all Armenian last names end in *-ian* or *-yan*, which mean "of" or "from." The roots of Armenian last names are a way to find out something about a person's family history. Roots can indicate the family trade generations ago, a family's geographic origins, or just the proper names of ancestors. The name Asbedian, for instance, means "son of a knight." Marashian, means "from Marash," which is a historic Armenian province, and Garabedian means, "son of Garabed." If the prefix *Ter-* stands in front of a name, such as in the Armenian president Levon Ter Petrossian's case, that means there was once a member of the clergy in the family. Last names that end in *-ouni*, such as Bagratouni, are also Armenian and show that the family tree can be traced to a noble family. Names that end in *-entz* or *-iantz* are also Armenian.

Common first names for girls are Alvard, Gohar, Narineh, and Nooneh. Armenian boys have names such as Ashot, Gagik, Nver, and Seyran. In the diaspora, girls are often named Ani, Knar, and Maral; and boys Aram, Raffi, Garo, and Vahe.

To show affection for someone, Armenians add the suffix *-jan* or *-eeg* to a person's name. Both mean "loved one" or "small one." Such versions of names or nicknames are called diminutives. The name Shoushan would be Shoushan-jan or Shousheeg. A name such as Ardashes might be shortened as a nickname to Ardash or Ardo. In the 1950s and 1960s, it was fashionable to give children names of characters from the plays of Shakespeare such as Hamlet and Ophelia. Names such as Svetlana or Sveta and Yuri came into fashion when the Soviet regime encouraged parents to give their children Russian names.

Armenian Artwork

People say that the soul of the Armenians is rooted in their art—whether visual, musical, or otherwise. Art has held a special place in the culture of the Armenian people for hundreds of years. In fact, in 1604, Shah Abbas, the ruler of Persia, conducted a forced migration, or movement, of over 300,000 Armenians to bring their knowledge and skills to his country.

Among the many different arts practiced by the Armenians are unique forms of architecture, metalwork and stone carving, sculpture, ceramics, frescoes (wall paintings), manuscript illumination (illustration) of the Bible, and jewelry making. Armenia's craft tradition is kept alive by thousands of people who paint, draw, weld, weave, carve, or sculpt for a living. Whatever the form of visual art, Armenians love to feature fruit, flowers, birds, crosses, and even the Armenian alphabet in their work.

Armenian church architecture represents the highest form of original Armenian art. Armenian churches feature distinctive multicornered and cone-shaped domes. Many are carved from mountain rock or made of volcanic *tuf* stone, which has the look and texture of a hardened sponge.

Armenia itself is often called an outdoor museum, because wherever you look, there are centuries-old, hand-cut monuments out in the open air. The *khatchkar,* or "cross stone," is one type of monument. A massive, upright slab of stone, a khatchkar is heavy but has a very delicate appearance. Originating in the Middle Ages, khatchkars feature large crosses with intricate and decorative designs etched into the flat rock, like lacework. They have been

used as tombstones, road markers, or even to commemorate historical events. No two are alike. These national treasures are found in church entranceways, at grave sites, or by themselves in the middle of a mountain meadow.

Painters and sculptors are active in Armenia today and exhibit their work in many settings. Artwork is often displayed at Vernissage, an outdoor bazaar that offers everything from automobile parts to backgammon sets inlaid with mother-of-pearl. Gifted artists often prefer to attract serious collectors through private studio exhibitions. In Armenia, artists such as Martiros Sarian and Yervand Kochar are highly respected for capturing the Armenian spirit in their art. Armenian artists are also known worldwide. The founder of the American modern art movement known as abstract expressionism was an Armenian named Arshile Gorky, born Vosdanik Adoian. Gorky's works are on display in many modern art museums.

Armenian Music

Armenian music is fascinating, as are the unusual-looking instruments Armenians play. The *oud*, a pear-shaped lute, sounds a bit like a mandolin. The *kemenchè*, another string instrument, looks like a big apple with a long stem attached and is played with a bow. The *kanun* is a form of zither. The *duduk* is a double-reeded wind instrument that looks like an oboe and makes a very somber but beautiful

A khatchkar

sound. The *dumbek* and *dahol* are drums made of metal or wood. Making music with these instruments is popular throughout the Near and Middle East, not just in Armenia.

In ancient and medieval times, Armenia had many troubadours and minstrels. These musicians traveled the countryside, composing and singing beautiful tunes about village life and the natural landscape. In modern times a gifted priest named Komitas Vardapet preserved what many people call the soul of Armenian music. In the late nineteenth century, Komitas traveled from village to village and listened to the peasants sing as they went about their daily chores. Komitas recorded what he heard. Before this the songs of the peasants were passed orally from generation to generation and were hardly known beyond the regions in which they were sung. Komitas's work came to an end, however, following the Armenian genocide of 1915. After witnessing the horrors of the massive effort to destroy the Armenian people, Komitas's own career and life were destroyed by mental illness. Only a fraction of the works of this musical genius survives today.

There are many different styles of Armenian music. Among them are church hymns, classical choral and orchestral music, opera, folk songs, dance music, and contemporary popular music. One of Armenia's great classical composers of modern times is Aram Khatchaturian. His fast-paced "Sabre Dance" from the *Gayne Ballet Suite*

Armenian instruments are in themselves works of art.

is known all over the world. Armen Tigranian is another remarkable Armenian composer. His *Davit Bek* opera chronicles the life and times of a hero who led the Armenian resistance in the troubled territory of Nagorno Karabagh in the 1700s. Some of the most celebrated classical singers and musicians in Armenia today include Hovhannes Badalian, Jivan Gasparian, Ophelia Hambartsumyan, and Rouben Matevosian.

Traditional Armenian musical theater is alive and well in Armenia, but more progressive sounds have strong followings, too. Modern-day troubadours such as Artur Meshjian and Roupen Hakhverdian perform for sold-out audiences. The flashy pop singer Harout Pamboukjian has many fans. Jazz musicians David Azarian and Datevik Hovanessian are well-known in international music circles. Younger Armenians love all kinds of music, especially jazz, heavy metal, and world music. In the United States and elsewhere, children enjoy songs sung by the Armenian-Canadian musician, Raffi, who made the children's song "Baby Beluga" famous.

Armenian Dance

The difficult mountainous terrain of Armenia has isolated its communities from one another. As a result, many have developed their own cultural practices. Armenian

Children folk dancing at a festival

dances, for example, are as diverse as the traditional costumes worn by people from different regions of historic Armenia. At celebrations, people may face each other and dance in a solo style, with men performing fancy footwork and the women making graceful gestures with their arms and wrists. Group dancing, in which people move in a line shoulder to shoulder or in a circle with their pinkie fingers linked, is also common. One dance from historic Armenia, the *tamzara,* is said to have been a favorite at festive gatherings generations ago. In the tamzara, dancers had to do a lot of traveling around the floor, which gave single people a chance to get a good look at everyone at the party.

Other Entertainment

Armenians enjoy formal entertainment such as concerts, plays, and films, but they also continue to rely on personal contact for entertainment. Although attention to mass media is growing in Armenia, most people spend little time watching television. Armenians much prefer gathering with relatives and friends to eat good food, tell stories, and sing and dance to traditional Armenian music. A party of this kind is known as a *kef*. A kef can take place in someone's apartment, by an ancient fortress in the foothills of the mountains, or on a picnic blanket in the wilderness. No special occasion is needed for people to throw a kef. In fact, the kef is such a natural part of life that every Armenian, young and old, is always ready to sing a solo, recite a poem, or play an instrument while others dance to make the get-together lively. A kef can easily turn into an all-day feast that lasts long into the night. If the kef is thrown to celebrate a birthday or religious holiday, it is not complete without a traditional lamb sacrifice, called a *madagh*. The madagh is a ritual that has been carried over from pre-Christian times. If the kef celebrates a special occasion such as a wedding or baptism, the animal might be taken to a church first to be blessed before being slaughtered.

Armenians do enjoy the cinema, and Russian, Armenian and even major American movies have been available for viewing for years. There have been fewer screenings in urban cinemas since the blockade and power shortage, however. Nevertheless, Armenians continue to produce films, and some have won international awards. Sergei Paradjanov is one award-winning Armenian filmmaker. Throughout his career Soviet authorities did their best to prevent Paradjanov from promoting "nationalistic" messages in his films by sending him to labor camps and prison. By doing so, the authorities managed to keep him from filmmaking for 15 years. But, despite government efforts to block his work, Paradjanov's films catapulted him to stardom. He became known as one of the greatest filmmakers of the USSR. Among his films are *Ashugh Gharib,* the story of a minstrel who sings his way across Armenia to win the hand of his beloved; *Color of Pomegranates,* a magical movie about an eighteenth century Armenian minstrel named Sayat Nova; *The Legend of Suram Fortress,* a picture based on a Georgian folk tale; and *Shadows of Our Forgotten Ancestors,* a film that recreates a Ukrainian legend.

Films have also been produced by Armenians in the diaspora. *Calendar,* a movie by the Egyptian-born Armenian named Atom Egoyan, gives viewers a taste of the beautiful panoramas in Armenia and the problems facing Armenians who no longer live in their homeland.

The Importance of Literature

Literature has always been important to the Armenian people. In fact, in 1638, Armenians helped establish the first printing house in the Middle East, in New Julfa, Iran. The eighteenth century was an important period of development for Armenian literature. Before then most books had been written in classical Armenian, which was not the language people generally used to speak to each other. As their contact with European and other societies increased, Armenian intellectuals became inspired by stories of the French Revolution and other popular movements designed to promote freedom, equality, and cultural expression. Armenian writers, along with artists, educators, and others, helped create and promote some of Armenia's best-known fables, anecdotes, plays, novels, short stories, poetry, and newspapers. Khatchadour Abovian (1805–1848) is considered the father of modern Armenian literature. His book, *The Wounds of Armenia,* was the first novel ever written in spoken Armenian, which could be understood by everyone, not just the very rich or educated. Raffi (born Hagop Melik-Hagopian) was the most celebrated novelist of the nineteenth century. His best known novel, *The Fool,* is an epic tale about important themes in Armenian life: family, honor, hard work, and national liberation. Literature has continued to be an important form of expression for Armenians. Writing was one of the ways that Armenians

A U.S. postage stamp honoring William Saroyan

resisted the Communists, although many writers who protested risked their lives doing so.

The Pulitzer Prize-winning American playwright William Saroyan is of Armenian heritage. He has also written many best-selling novels and short stories. Saroyan's works include *The Time of Your Life, The Human Comedy,* and *The Daring Young Man on the Flying Trapeze.* Many of the characters in his stories are based on colorful people he met and befriended. Born in Fresno, California, in 1908, Saroyan also wrote a humorous book called *My Name Is Aram* that drew from his own experiences growing up as the son of Armenian immigrants.

A History of Survival

Throughout most of its history, Armenia has been a conquered land. Empires in the West and East—from the Parthians, Romans, Byzantines, and Arabs to the Persians, Mongols, Turks, and Russians—were almost always at war, trying to capture land and riches beyond their own territories. Armenia often stood between them. Sometimes the empire builders and their forces dealt with the Armenians savagely, capturing rulers, seizing women and enslaving men, looting treasuries, and trying to convert the people to their religion. At other times, they made treaties with the Armenian kings and used Armenia's mountains as a shield against their own enemies. This was an intolerable situation for the Armenian people. At worst, the invasions threatened to destroy them. At best, conquests affected the development of their civilization in unpredictable ways. Peasants and masons, who normally tilled fields and built bridges, had to defend their homes constantly, fight in the army, or flee to safer areas.

Although Armenia experienced periods of great prosperity and cultural growth, such progress was usually overshadowed by years of foreign occupation. Under cruel dictators, life in Armenia was bleak. Armenian nobles were

Mountains—the great natural barriers of Armenia

taken as hostages to ensure obedience. Peasants had to pay tribute, or special taxes, giving up their worldly possessions, their farm animals, and, under the most ruthless occupiers, even their own children in order to escape death.

Geography's Role

Since ancient times the location of Armenia has made it a valuable land. Armenia stood at the intersection of the powerful empires of Europe, Asia, and the Middle East on an important trading route. The route was called the Silk Road, because silk from the East passed over it with merchants traveling to the West. The exchange of goods from different regions made many local lords and tradespeople in Armenia wealthy as toll collectors. Trade also linked Armenia with other cultures. Customs and ideas of other civilizations traveled over the Silk Road in the form of Greek plays and Eastern philosophies. The exchange of ideas taught the Armenian people much about the rest of the world, and they sometimes adopted new beliefs and practices as their own.

There were many advantages to being located at the crossroads of East and West, but Armenia's location also brought its share of misfortune to its inhabitants. Neighboring peoples often sought to capture the riches that passed over the Silk Road. In addition, the geography of historic Armenia invited invaders to capture and occupy Armenian communities that would serve their military aims. The rocky mountains of the Taurus, Pontus, and Caucasus ranges protected Armenia's lowlands and were natural barriers. However, the mountains kept Armenian communities from uniting and becoming a force to be reckoned with.

To make things worse, for centuries Armenia was ruled not by one supreme king but by many princes, called *nakharars*. Each nakharar had a realm of his own to govern. Rather than submit to one ruler, the nakharars often feuded among themselves for status and authority. In ancient and medieval times, they were frequently forced to obey more powerful states such as Persia or Rome.

Yet, although Armenia's geography was a handicap in many ways, the many minor "kingdoms" separated by rugged mountains proved to be an advantage in some ways. There were so many self-contained districts in Armenia, that even if invaders raided and destroyed key Armenian population centers, they could never wipe out the entire Armenian race. At the same time, geographic and political divisions encouraged the growth of distinct Armenian subcultures. Traces of many of these subcultures are evident even today in unique dialects, ways of dress, food, and other cultural features.

The First Armenians

Language studies have shown that the forerunners of the Armenian people lived on what is called the Anatolian plateau since at least 1300 B.C. Among the first tribes to occupy these lands were the Hayasas and Nayiris. These groups merged to form the kingdom of Urartu. Urartu stretched from the Euphrates River in the west to regions near the Caspian Sea in the east, Lake Urmia in the south, and the Caucasus region in the north. According to ancient documents, the first Urartian king was called Aram, and the capital of the kingdom was Tushpa (present-day Van). The Urartians built major cities, canals, castles, and forts. There was rich farmland with orchards and vineyards. During this early period, Armenia was a metalworking center—one of the first in the world. Coins, tools, weapons, and jewelry were made there.

In ancient times people around the world wanted to explain why the seasons changed, why the sun rose and set, why the rains came, why winds blew, and many other forces of nature. Armenians and other peoples believed that these natural events were directed by powerful gods. The Armenians built temples, sacrificed animals, and held many festivals to pay tribute to the gods. By 500 B.C., Armenians had assigned names to their gods. One of their favorites was the goddess of fertility and wisdom, whom they named Anahit. They prayed for Anahit to bless their land and their women so that they would produce healthy crops and children.

Tigran the Great

By the first century before the birth of Christ, Armenia had been split into different parts. Some regions fell under various Persian rulers, others into Roman hands. A young Armenian prince of the Ardashesian royal family, named Tigran II, had grown up as a royal hostage, or *tayyagvorti,* in the Persian kingdom of Parthia. Under this arrangement, which kept the Armenians bound to the Parthians, noble offspring grew sympathetic to the rival family that raised them. They would usually be married to a member of their adoptive families and would return to their own clan when they reached adulthood. These ties helped keep peace between hostile families and strengthened alliances between them.

In 95 B.C., when word reached the kingdom of Parthia that Tigran's father had died, Tigran was proclaimed king of Armenia. Tigran had studied military tactics under the Parthians. When he returned to Armenia for the first time since his childhood, he was determined to unite the kingdom's eastern and western regions. Under Tigran and his disciplined army, Armenian forces embarked on a campaign of conquest. They marched from the Black Sea to the Caspian Sea and from Mesopotamia (today's Iraq) to

King Tigran is featured on the 500 Dram note.

Phoenicia (today's Lebanon) and Syria. Tigran subdued many neighboring powers and created an empire that for a brief time was second only to Rome. He was soon dubbed Tigran the Great. The famous Roman writer Cicero recalled that Tigran "made the republic of Rome tremble before his powerful arms." To keep peace between nations, Tigran married the daughter of Mithridates, king of Pontus. A keen monarch, Tigran developed great centers of culture and learning. He named his new capital Tigranakert, meaning "built by Tigran," although much of it was built by slaves drawn from captured enemy armies. Even today the name of Tigran the Great is a symbol of strength and national unity for the Armenians.

King Trdat and Saint Gregory the Illuminator

During the reign of King Trdat (Tiridates) III, in the third century A.D., Christianity had begun to spread and gain strength as a religion. Even so, many rich and powerful kings and pagan priests still prayed to their own gods and saw the new religion and its followers as a threat. They put Armenians and others who pledged their faith in Christ to death. King Trdat was shocked to learn one day that one of his nobles named Gregory was the long-lost son of Prince Anak, who had killed Trdat's father in battle. To make matters worse, Gregory was a Christian and refused to lay wreaths in honor of the gods. The king became furious. He had Gregory thrown into a deep, dark pit, where he remained for 14 years.

While he was imprisoned, Gregory managed to survive on morsels of bread a kind woman secretly tossed him every day. During these long years King Trdat fell in love with a beautiful Christian girl named Hripsimè. She refused to marry him. In a rage Trdat had Hripsimè and other followers of Christ put to death, after which he went insane. When no physician was able to treat the king, Trdat's sister dreamed that only Gregory could heal him. The following day Gregory was brought before Trdat. The two spoke in private for days. Gregory's words cured the troubled king. Trdat was so inspired by Christian teachings that he converted to Christianity. His noble court followed his example.

In A.D. 301, Armenia became the first nation in the world to proclaim Christianity its state religion. Gregory became the spiritual leader, or catholicos, of the

Armenians. He also had the Etchmiadzin Cathedral built. Today the cathedral is one of the oldest Christian churches in the world. Gregory is known as the Illuminator because he enlightened the Armenian people with Christian teachings. The site of the pit in which he was thrown by Trdat, located within the walls of Khor Virap Monastery, remains one of the most sacred sites in the country.

Saint Mesrob Mashdots

Until the fifth century the Armenian people wrote their language in Greek, Syriac, and other alphabets. As the Byzantines and Persians were still trying to lay claim to parts of Armenia, King Vramshabu and Catholicos Sahag decided that the Armenians should have an alphabet of their own. They asked a devoted scholar and clergyman named Mesrob Mashdots to create an alphabet so that people could write in Armenian. In the year 406 he presented them with an alphabet of 36 letters. (Two more were added later.) The development of the alphabet ushered in what was to become the golden age of Armenian literature. The Roman and Persian rulers of the day permitted Mesrob to open schools and teach the alphabet to the nobility and the masses. It took time for the Armenians to learn to read and write, but the alphabet helped them keep their unique culture alive through literature. Mesrob Mashdots also helped develop the Georgian and Caucasian Albanian alphabets.

The Armenian alphabet and its creator

Saint Vardan Mamikonian

Seeing that Christianity was spreading throughout Armenia, the Sassanid dynasty of Persia invaded Armenia to put a stop to it. Although some Armenians were still pagans, many others had become Christian and united with each other to present a real threat to Persian control of Armenia. When the Armenians refused to submit to Zoroastrianism, a fire-worshiping religion, in A.D. 451, the army of King Yazdegerd II of Persia met Armenians in battle. General Vardan Mamikonian, a powerful Armenian nobleman, delivered a great testimony to the Persians. He

Saint Vardan leading his army in defense of Christianity

stated that the Armenians would never renounce Christianity. His words were met with the sword. The Persian army arrived on the Avarayr battlefield equipped with armored elephants and catapult machines. Greatly outnumbered, Vardan and his army valiantly fought to the death to protect their right to practice their chosen faith. Many Armenians, including General Vardan, were killed in the battle, which came to be known as the Battle of Vardanantz, after the martyrs of Vardan. In spite of the huge loss of life, the battle was a moral victory for the Armenians. They demonstrated a fierce dedication to their beliefs—and won their freedom in the end. As minor battles continued to be waged over the next decades, the Persians lost many warriors and finally decided to abandon their plan to convert the Armenians. They signed the Treaty of Nuvarsak, which permitted religious and social freedom for all Armenians. Today many churches are named after Vardan and his followers, who are among Armenia's most courageous saints.

Dynasties and Ottoman Rule

From the fifth century to the eleventh century, several Armenian royal families passed power from one generation to the next. These ruling families who held onto power for generations were called dynasties. Each family ruled a region of Armenia. While they ruled with authority, they often had to answer to higher powers in the Persian and Byzantine Empires and the Arab Caliphate. When Turkic hordes from Central Asia appeared on the scene from the south and east, Armenians were once again at the mercy of these marauders. From the eleventh to the eighteenth century, Armenia was dominated by such groups as Turkmen, Seljuk Turks, Mongols, Ottoman Turks, and Persians.

Over the years such groups aimed to control Armenia and other lands in the region. Suddenly, however, the Turks and Arabs became allies when the Turks officially converted to Islam. By the sixteenth century the Ottoman Turks had conquered most of Asia Minor, including Armenia. By the 1800s it had become standard practice for non-Turks to be treated as second-class citizens in the Ottoman Empire. This meant that people such as Jews, Greeks, and Armenians did not have the same rights and privileges that Turkish subjects had. Armenians often had to pay extremely high taxes, could not testify in court, were forbidden to carry arms, and could not build new homes or renovate their churches. Under the Ottoman Turks, Armenians put their homes, jobs, and themselves at risk if they spoke their native language openly, allowed women in their families to appear in public without covering their faces, or sent their children to Armenian schools. Militant Turks were at work within the government to expand the borders of Turkey as far as possible, unite all Turkic peoples in one empire, and rid their empire of any groups that were not Turks.

Many Armenians at this time lived as peasants in the rough, mountainous terrain of eastern Anatolia. Many also lived in Constantinople (present-day Istanbul), which became the capital of the Ottoman Empire. The more than 250,000 Armenians who lived in Constantinople worked in respected fields, such as architecture, banking, business, and civil service. The Turks were said to resent the prosperity many Armenian city dwellers enjoyed.

By the 1800s the Ottoman Empire, which stretched as far as North Africa, had begun to fall apart. Corruption increased, people had difficulty earning a living, and social unrest was felt everywhere. Ethnic and religious minority groups living within the empire's borders were blamed for these misfortunes. The government of Turkey, under the rule of Sultan Abdul Hamid II, began to organize pogroms, or mass killings, of Armenians. When the Armenian people began to demand social improvements, the sultan responded by ordering further massacres. Over 200,000 Armenians were killed between 1894 and 1908. Even when a new government seized power, the persecution of Armenians continued, and conditions in Turkey got worse rather than better. In response to this, many ethnic groups living under Ottoman rule took matters into their own hands. They wanted the right to protect and govern themselves, through armed resistance if necessary.

The Darkest Page in Armenian History

In a secret meeting new leaders of the Young Turk party plotted to exterminate the Armenians who lived under Ottoman Turkish rule. When World War I broke out in 1914, Turkey's military leaders decided to do away with the Armenians, a people who did not fit into their plans. On April 24, 1915, Talaat Pasha, the Turkish minister of the interior, ordered the elimination of all Armenians living in the empire. The elimination of the Armenians had been planned carefully so that it would not be noticed. The major powers of the world would not pay attention, the Turks thought, because they were caught up in a world war.

One of the first orders given by the Young Turks was to round up all the leading male Armenian intellectuals, such as teachers, writers, and civil servants. These individuals would be eliminated first so that the Armenians would have no leadership to guide them. Special Turkish forces rounded up hundreds of community leaders from all over the empire and marched them to remote places where the international community could not observe them. There they shot them. Thousands of Armenian men were forced to join the Ottoman army. In reality they formed labor battalions. These Armenians were worn down by hard labor and hunger and then were forced to dig their own graves at gunpoint before they were shot.

The Young Turks had convicts and murderers released

Armenians are marched out of town under the guard of armed Turkish soldiers during the genocide of 1915.

from Turkish prisons and organized into special military units to carry out the plan of genocide, or mass killing of the Armenians. With the help of Kurdish bandits, these special units terrorized the Armenian people, looted their towns, uprooted women and children from their homes, and drove them on death marches into the Syrian desert. Any Turkish official who refused orders to take part in the massacres was immediately killed or replaced.

According to the testimony of foreign diplomats, missionaries, and teachers, the slaughter of the innocent Armenians was not only widespread but horrifying. Women and children were raped and sold into slavery. People were skinned alive, their nails and tongues torn out.

Others had nails hammered into their feet like horseshoes. Witnesses recalled how Turkish officers would throw babies into flames or would bind groups of Armenians together, pour gasoline over them, and burn them alive. Because it was strictly forbidden for anyone to help the Armenians, tens of thousands died from thirst, starvation, exposure, and disease.

Those who survived the massacres have been haunted throughout their lives by sickening memories of those years. In his book *Some of Us Survived: The Story of an Armenian Boy,* Kerop Bedoukian tells how as a nine-year-old he had to brave inhuman conditions in order to stay alive. He recalls his mother dressing his older brother up as a girl to save him from sure death, and how, starving and filthy, he himself watched everyone around him die.

During the massacres, teachers and missionaries working in Turkey witnessed the slaughters and notified their respective ambassadors. The diplomats then appealed to the Turkish government to put a stop to the killings. Among them was Henry Morgenthau, U.S. ambassador to Turkey, who wired to the United States that a campaign of extermination was in progress. Unfortunately these pleas did not stop the massacres.

Articles criticizing the killings appeared regularly in newspapers around the world, including *The New York Times.* In fact, the genocide was so well-known in the United

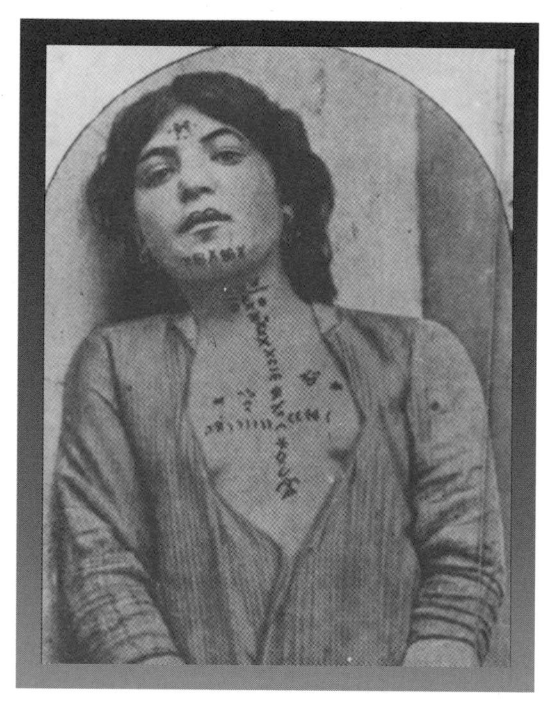

This rescued Armenian girl had been sold into a Turkish harem during the massacres. The tattoos on her face and body name all her previous "owners."

States that American children grew up hearing their parents persuade them to clean their dinner plates because there were "starving Armenians" in the Ottoman Empire denied food and drink. The Near East Relief Fund was set up in the United States to provide emergency relief for people forced from their homes in Anatolia. Through contributions from concerned Americans, the organization raised $25 million and saved the lives of thousands of suffering Armenians by providing them with food, clothing, and shelter.

Soon after Armenians were forcibly removed from their homes, the Turkish state declared their lands abandoned and rewarded those who participated in the massacres with stolen goods and properties. Meanwhile, hundreds of Armenian churches and monasteries in Turkey were destroyed. Many others were converted to animal stables and even prisons. All in all, 1.5 million or more than half of the Armenians living in the Ottoman Empire perished in this merciless campaign.

Stripped of their families, homes, and dignity, the survivors and their children still suffer indignities today. The government of Turkey was never punished for this crime, and the present regime in Turkey denies that the genocide was ever committed. Heads of state and genocide survivors alike agree that the deep emotional scars left from the massacres will not begin to heal until the current regime in Turkey admits to what the past regime did.

Armenia in the Twentieth Century

When Czar Nicholas II, the ruler of Russia, was a killed in 1918, countries neighboring Russia fell into chaos. Armenians once again fought off Turkish advances to take what remained of their homeland and declared their independence in 1918. With little money or labor to work with, the republic struggled to stay in operation, holding elections, finding people jobs, and establishing governmental relations—all while in a state of economic collapse.

Very few able-bodied men had survived the massacres, and refugees were everywhere. Hunger, poverty, and disease plagued the country.

As Turkey and Russia sought to divide Armenia between themselves, promises from England, France, and the United States to protect Armenia were not kept. While the Western countries turned their interests elsewhere, Turkey made a secret treaty with Russia. Both powers were closing in on the small piece of Armenia that remained. As the Turkish empire continued to expand from the west, Armenia faced the end. Fearing complete ruin, Armenia surrendered to the Soviet army in 1920. In 1921 it won its independence for a brief period when a popular revolt overthrew Communist rule. The same year, however, Armenia was taken over once again by the Communists and was incorporated into the new Union of Soviet Socialist Republics (USSR).

Communism—An Instrument of Change

When the Bolshevik political party came to power in 1917, the political and social system it introduced created a way of life that would endure in most of Eastern Europe and Central Asia for more than 70 years. The system and way of life the Bolsheviks created was based on communism. According to Communist theory, society's problems developed from the conflicting values and attitudes that existed between business owners and workers and between people of different social rank. Communist leaders such as Vladimir Lenin promised to bring equal opportunities to all—whether they were scientists or street sweepers—rather than just to a few, and to eliminate ill will between people. To achieve this, the Communist plan was to create a society with no class distinctions. Under this new system institutions such as schools, hospitals, and newspapers were to be owned by the government. Private ownership would be forbidden. Government control also quickly spread to other parts of people's lives, however. Open criticism of the government was not permitted. Travel to non-Communist countries was banned, and information and literature from non-Communist nations, such as the United States, were censored.

The Soviet Command

When the USSR was established, more than 25 different nationalities spread across two continents were brought under one central government. Over many years 15 republics came to be a part of the USSR. Many did not join the USSR willingly. The many different nationalities and republics, each with its distinct heritage and resources, made the USSR a very diverse and powerful empire. Under Josef Stalin, however, a policy of Russification was pursued in which the unique customs and practices of the different peoples of the USSR were replaced by Russian ways. Although Russification created a common ground for people from very different cultures, Soviet citizens resented the policy because it discouraged them from preserving the traditions and customs of their ancestors.

As industry developed at a rapid pace all over the Soviet Union, Armenia developed one of the highest standards of living among the republics. Armenia also distinguished itself during World War II. Some 500,000 Armenians served in the Soviet armed forces during the war, and about 100,000 of those were decorated with medals for their contribution to the effort to crush the Nazi German regime. Even today Armenian marshal Ivan Baghramian is well remembered for his military leadership during the war.

In 1947 about 100,000 Armenians from all over the world returned to their homeland for the first time since the genocide. Even though these people were sure to bring ideas that would clash with Soviet thinking, the Communist party encouraged the move. The Soviet workforce needed a boost because many Soviet workers had lost their lives in World War II. Many other Armenians in the diaspora, however, did not return. They were suspicious about how life in the USSR would be. Indeed, many patriotic Armenians from abroad were persecuted for their ideas once they returned to settle in the Soviet Union. The government under Stalin severely punished anyone who seemed to defy Stalin's authority.

Gorbachev and Reform

By the late 1980s the shortcomings of the Communist system could no longer be ignored. Much of the USSR's income had been spent meeting the needs of the military, and the Soviet population suffered as a result. There were shortages of food and clothing. Outdated technology could not fulfill people's needs. People were frustrated because they could not openly express their feelings or ideas if they did not agree with Soviet thinking.

Recognizing that change could not be avoided, Mikhail Gorbachev, chairman of the Soviet Union, proposed reforms that would bring a greater level of efficiency and tolerance to the Communist system. Gorbachev introduced the concepts of *glasnost* (openness in the media) and *perestroika* (rebuilding to restore prosperity). He believed that these policies would help improve the quality of life in the Soviet Union and keep the republics united. When Gorbachev's plan was put into effect, people began to feel freer to express their discontent. As a result, long-time rivalries between republics over land resurfaced, and the different peoples of the Soviet Union began to assert their national identities.

During the Soviet period, all sorts of shortages made waiting in line routine—as in this case, for fuel.

The Armenian Earthquake

Just as change had begun to come to the Soviet Union, Armenia suffered a crushing blow. At 11:41 A.M. on December 7, 1988, roads began to shake, water pipes exploded, and the ground opened up and devoured buildings, cars, and people. Armenia had been struck by a massive natural disaster—an earthquake. High-rise apartment and office buildings swayed. Many buildings collapsed, crushing the people inside. Many perished, including firefighters and doctors. Few specialists survived to rescue and treat the trapped and wounded people. Those who did survive used their bare hands to reach people caught under the rubble until cranes arrived to pull them out.

When the disaster hit, the Soviet authorities were unprepared to deal with such a widespread emergency and did not respond quickly. Their efforts were poorly organized and plagued with delays. The town of Spitak, located at the quake's epicenter, was totally destroyed, as were more than 50 other villages, more than 500 schools, and thousands of factories, community centers, clinics, and stores. Makeshift hospitals and homes were built to save the more than 520,000 homeless people from the bitter cold. Many survivors with no place else to go lived in "generator units," which were like oversized oil drums. Orphanages were needed to care for children who had lost their parents. Trauma centers had to be set up to treat the

Over 40 percent of Armenia was damaged by the earthquake of 1988.

people whose injuries had been disabling or who went into shock or severe depression after the tragedy.

Fortunately there was a ray of hope for Armenia. Because of glasnost the international press was able to tell the world about the disaster. In the first six months after the earthquake, more than $500 million in aid was sent to Armenia. Sympathetic people and social welfare groups from more than 100 countries around the world rushed to help the stricken country. Heavy coats, blankets, canned foods, and even prefabricated homes were shipped to Armenia. Famous singers, such as Charles Aznavour and Placido Domingo, raised money for Armenia through their performances.

Although these kind gestures helped the Armenians and showed them that they were not alone, they provided only a portion of the sort of assistance Armenia needed. The Soviet authorities promised to rebuild the devastated areas, but the collapse of the Soviet Union soon after the earthquake brought government-sponsored reconstruction efforts to a halt. Today, reconstruction efforts still proceed at a slow pace because of the ongoing economic blockade and energy shortage.

Nagorno Karabagh

Meanwhile, an entirely different development was also shaking the nation. A territorial issue that had been suppressed since 1923 was reemerging. Armenians were demanding that the historic Armenian land internationally referred to as Nagorno Karabagh be reunited with Armenia.

In 1923, Josef Stalin had awarded several Armenian territories, including Nagorno Karabagh, to the neighboring republic of Azerbaijan. This act greatly disturbed the Armenians. More than 90 percent of the people in Nagorno Karabagh were Armenians. They had lived for centuries on the southeastern edge of the Armenian plateau. Now, they had been cut off from their homeland. They unanimously opposed Stalin's move. According to the arrangement, Nagorno Karabagh's new rulers were Azeris, a minority population. The Armenian inhabitants of Nagorno Karabagh made up the majority population. Although the Soviet republics were supposed to provide equal rights to all their inhabitants, regardless of nationality, they did not always do so. In the decades leading up to the 1990s, Armenians living under Azeri rule were not permitted to practice their religion freely or give their children Armenian names. The issue was not only a question of religious or ethnic differences, however. The Armenians of Nagorno Karabagh saw their struggle as a fight for national liberation. The Armenians of Nagorno Karabagh had held on to their wish to be reincorporated into the republic of Armenia for decades.

The Armenians had contained their feelings for a long time, but with the arrival of glasnost they could demand equal rights. In both Nagorno Karabagh and Armenia, Armenians took to the streets by the thousands, peacefully petitioning the Soviet central government for change. Unfortunately their efforts were met with indifference, hostility, even brutal repression. The Soviet leadership in Moscow condemned the movement, while Azerbaijan's leadership, threatened by the move, responded with violent assaults on unarmed Armenians. It soon became clear that the dispute could not be resolved peacefully, and Armenians throughout Nagorno Karabagh took up arms to fight for their freedom. At the beginning of 1992,

Armenians have taken up arms to defend their rights in Nagorno Karabagh.

Armenians set up the independent Republic of Karabagh, which is connected to Armenia by a small strip of land called the Lachin Corridor. Nagorno Karabagh is roughly 1,700 square miles (4,400 square kilometers) in area—about the size of Delaware. The name *Nagorno* means "mountainous," and *Karabagh* means "fertile black gardens." Today, many Armenians choose to call the territory by its ancient Armenian name, Artsakh, and often repeat the motto "Our people are our mountains."

Negotiations continue over the territory. Armenians in Nagorno Karabagh wish to govern themselves on their own terms and have begun the long process of setting up national institutions, such as a parliament and a university. The Azerbaijanis, however, still want Nagorno Karabagh for themselves. As a result there has been great instability in both Armenia and Azerbaijan, and a blockade has been imposed on Armenia by its neighbors Azerbaijan and Turkey. The authorities of Armenia, Nagorno Karabagh, and Azerbaijan realize that an end to hostilities is the only way that economic development and progress can be ensured for both countries. But only time will tell what the future holds.

From Turmoil to Transition

By 1991 many Soviet soldiers were abandoning their posts throughout the Soviet Union, and it had become even more difficult for the Soviet government to control unrest. In August 1991, a circle of Communists who disagreed with Gorbachev's new policies tried to take over the government in Moscow. In response, thousands of Russian citizens stormed the government offices in Moscow and forced the circle of Communists to give up. Within days the people had gained control.

In Armenia, people called for popular elections. On September 21, 1991, 99 percent of Armenian citizens went to the polls and voted that Armenia should declare its independence from the USSR. On October 16 of the same

Armenians took to the streets in 1991 to demand independence.

year, presidential elections were held, and Levon Ter Petrossian was elected president of the new independent republic of Armenia, capturing 83 percent of the vote. Before being elected, Ter Petrossian had been a scholar and political activist. He and other academics had formed a group called the Karabagh Committee. They organized mass demonstrations calling for the reunification of Nagorno Karabagh with Armenia.

In Moscow later that year, the people elected Russian statesman Boris Yeltsin as president to lead the newly independent Russian republic. When the Soviet Union dissolved in December of 1991, 11 of the 15 former Soviet states signed an agreement to create a loose federation called the Commonwealth of Independent States (CIS).

The CIS states had grown to depend on each other for economic support over the years. They believed that the Commonwealth would benefit them all. They would continue to work hand in hand and at the same time maintain their political and cultural independence. One of the Commonwealth's aims was to divide and distribute the resources of the former Soviet Union among the republics in a fair and equal way. The CIS also laid the foundation for greater cooperation among the states, helping the republics establish trade relations with each other, for example.

The old system had collapsed. In 1992 the independent nations embarked on a new way of life. They would have access to information, goods, and other nations as never before. Since 1992 the former states of the Soviet Union have come to see that their newfound freedom brings its own set of challenges. Coping with independent statehood has not been easy. Although many political scientists are making predictions about the future of the former Soviet republics, it is still too early to tell what is in store for Armenia and the other independent states. What is certain is that every one of the newly independent states is struggling to make the transformation work. All hope that the shift to independence will last and that it will not be remembered as yet another short phase in world history.

Legends, Folk Tales, and Sayings

Legends have their place in history, too. Legends are often woven from real stories about real people and usually encourage national pride. The oral tradition is an important part of the Armenian national culture. Before events were recorded in writing, troubadours and minstrels recited and sang stories about people and their accomplishments. These stories were passed from one generation to the next.

A Dynasty of Daredevils

Armenian legends capture the courageous spirit as well as the tragic history of the Armenian people. Armenians see parts of themselves in their legendary heroes, who boast superhuman strength and endurance but display very human flaws. Five such heroes are described together in the epic *David of Sassoun.* This story, which is thousands of years old, features the exploits of David, Big Mher and Little Mher, and the twin strongmen Sanasar and Balthazar. In one episode Sanasar sets out to marry the beautiful "Princess of Forty Braids." After risking his life slaying dragons and fetching rare treasures from faraway lands,

Sanasar completes seven death-defying tests to claim the princess as his wife. When Sanasar reaches the princess's castle, he outsmarts Hamdol, a sinister creature with supernatural powers who guards the gates. Sanasar overwhelms Hamdol by shaking his hand and squeezing his lifeblood out of his fingernails!

Haik Nahapet

Armenian legend says that Armenians call themselves Hai because they are the children of Haik Nahapet, the founding father of the Armenian nation. According to legend, Haik was a great-grandson of the Biblical Noah. Having first lived in Armenia like their ancestors, Haik and his people decided to resettle in Babylon. They became so disgusted with the evils of that place, however, that they decided to return to Armenia. Bel, the tyrant of Babylon, commanded Haik to stay. When Haik defied his orders, Bel gathered his army and pursued the Armenians. Although Haik had just a small tribe and Bel an army of thousands, Haik was a fine archer. He slew Bel with his bow and arrow and sent Bel's men fleeing to Babylon. Haik and his people returned to their homeland. The Armenian people love and respect the legendary Haik for saving his people and creating the Armenian nation.

The legendary vishap

The Fearsome Vishap

Long before Armenians practiced Christianity, they believed that good and evil spirits ruled the earth and controlled the weather. One of the evil spirits that ancient Armenians recognized was a sea monster called a *vishap* who dwelled in the deep, blue waters of Lake Van. This vicious sea dragon was described as having scales like a fish and up to seven heads. Every time one of Lake Van's violent storms would boil up, the locals would say that it was the vishap's short temper erupting. According to legend, the vishap grew and grew until he was big enough to swallow up the world. Vahagn, the dragon-slaying god, is credited with hunting down the vishap in the deeps of Lake Van, hurling it into the burning sun, and saving humanity. As feared as the vishap was, Armenian knights were fond of the fierce monster. They would carry silk banners with the image of the vishap on it into battle as a sign of power and courage.

Ara the Fair

There once was a brave and handsome Armenian king named Ara. The powerful Shamiram, queen of neighboring Assyria, heard of his courage and beauty and sent her ambassadors to convince Ara to marry her. Happily married already and suspicious of Shamiram's motives, Ara refused her offer. Enraged, Shamiram declared war on Armenia and ordered her warriors to bring Ara back to her alive. During the fighting Ara dressed as a common soldier so that he would not be noticed. Because of his masquerade one of Shamiram's men accidentally killed him. Horrified by the news, Shamiram had Ara's dead body placed on an altar in her castle. For days and nights she never left his side. She brought the royal hounds to lick his wounds and plastered him with special ointments, praying to the gods to revive

Queen Shamiram gazes at the corpse of King Ara the Fair.

him. When he did not come back to life, Shamiram grieved for a long time and finally buried his body. In tribute to Ara's memory, Shamiram built palaces and fortresses in the beautiful region of Van and spent her summers there.

Fables and Folk Tales

In Armenia both children and adults love to hear and tell fables and folk tales. A fable is called a *hekyat* in Armenian. A hekyat may be full of magic and talking animals and have a moral or lesson. Folk tales are often told just to entertain. There are many different tales and storytelling styles from the regions of present-day and historic Armenia, but they all have a common bond. Folk tales use both humor and wisdom to show the merits and flaws in people's character. Traditionally Armenian folk tales start with the words *There once was and was not in ancient Armenia* and end with a variety of phrases, such as *They reached their purpose, and may we reach ours* or *The boy wed the girl, and they celebrated for seven days and seven nights.* Here is one example.

Advice From a Poor Man

There once was and was not a farmer going to market, carrying grain on his donkey's back. Along the way he passed a thin and hungry-looking man on the side of the road. The young man stopped the farmer and said,

"I couldn't help noticing the way that you have your donkey loaded down with grain. I see that you have two large sacks of grain hanging on one side of the donkey, and a large rock tied with rope on the other side of the donkey."

"I always do it that way to balance the donkey," replied the farmer.

"I'm sure that's so," replied the young man, "but you are weighing down the donkey unnecessarily! Why don't you divide the sacks so that you have one on each side? You can get rid of the rock and lighten the donkey's load."

This made good sense to the farmer, who started to untie the rope. He said, "You're a smart young fellow, you must be rich!"

"Not at all," said the young man. "I'm just a poor schoolteacher."

The farmer stopped, looked the scrawny man over, and started to retie the ropes as they were before. He said, "Compared to you, I'm pretty well off, so I think I'll stick to doing things my way."

Sayings With Feeling

Armenian sayings are very colorful. Many of them help people get through rough situations and see the brighter side of things. The phrases *Tsavut danem* and

Gyankit mernem are heard all over the nation in many situations. They are used to show affection or to ask someone to go out of his or her way for you. The first means "May I take away your pain," and the second, "May I die for you" to emphasize that the person would return the favor if he or she could. All over the country, friends and people who have never met before call each other "dear brother" or "sister," *aghper* or *kooyrig jan.*

If you ask an Armenian "How are you?" he or she will undoubtedly reply by saying *vochinch.* The reply means "It's of no consequence" or, more simply, "Not bad." This saying originated during Soviet days, when answering "I'm fine" would arouse suspicion about why, during hard times, someone was doing so well. If someone were to reply, "Things are terrible," however, the authorities would have the person quickly shipped off to a labor camp in Siberia, where discontented people were sent to work under harsh conditions. Thus, by saying *vochinch,* people could avoid committing themselves to danger.

Armenians in the diaspora also repeat time-worn sayings passed down from their refugee ancestors. When something is long overdue, some Armenians say *Oosh lini, noosh lini,* which means "Let it be late, as long as it's sweet." Another common phrase is *Dzoor nusdink, shidag khosink.* It means "Let's sit crooked but talk straight." When someone is exhausted or has had a setback, he or she may say *Mookhus maretzav,* which means "My smoke was extinguished." Since ovens are considered a necessity for food and heat, if someone's smoke goes out, they are in dire straits!

Here are a few more sayings, translated from the Armenian. Many are humorous or show wisdom. They are meant to teach and uplift people during hard times. Armenians love to use animals and nature to illustrate a point.

- When the herd reversed direction, the lame became the leaders.
- A wildflower on the mountaintop will not trade places with the rose in the garden.
- Spit against the wind, and you spit in your own face.
- The camel does not see his own hump.
- Let a loved one be alive, though seven mountains away.
- The bread you eat by your own sweat is better than the dishes of sultans.

5

Holidays and Special Occasions

Armenia's most widely honored celebrations are religious holidays. Although some of these festive occasions have a lot in common with holidays celebrated around the world, many Armenian holidays still include rituals from pagan times. During the Soviet years many Christian holidays and observances were discontinued. The Soviet authorities were somewhat successful in their attempts to cut people off from religion, but many people quietly clung to their religious beliefs all the while. Today Armenians practice their religion openly. In today's more open society, old and new generations of Armenians are becoming reacquainted with the church.

The most important religious holidays for Armenians are Christmas and Easter. Christmas is celebrated on January 6 as an entirely religious holiday. Families go to churches in their neighborhoods and celebrate the birth and the baptism of Jesus all at once. During the Soviet years Father Winter would come to every child's house on New Year's Eve, bearing gifts. The following morning children would find sweets such as dried nuts and fruits under their pillows, and other gifts would surround their beds. At a time when Armenians were discouraged from practicing their religion, the New Year's holiday had more of a winter theme than a religious one. Today families still give gifts on New Year's Day and during the holiday period. Children receive toys and candy from the same old man, who is now called Father Christmas. Adults exchange gifts such as silver trinkets, flowers, and brandy.

More than forty days before Easter, Armenians traditionally begin observing Lent. At this time people deny themselves the pleasure of eating meat and dairy products. This practice helps people understand better the hardships that Jesus endured in the time leading up to his crucifixion. On Easter, Armenians celebrate the resurrection of Jesus.

A long-standing Easter tradition is the coloring of Easter eggs. Eggs are boiled in water with red onionskins. The eggs turn a deep red, which symbolizes the blood of Christ. During the festivities of Easter Sunday, adults and children have boiled-egg duels in which they tap the tips of each other's eggs. The champion is the one whose egg does not crack during the contest. It is customary for some families to prepare a traditional egg salad dish once the duels are over. The more religious families in Armenia gather up the eggshells once the eggs have been cracked, and bury them in the earth. Since the red dye symbolizes the blood of Christ, it is considered sacrilegious to throw the shells away.

Vartivar

Vartivar is a fun holiday that goes back to pre-Christian times. In those early days Armenians paid their respects to the goddess Anahit by exhibiting their handicrafts or reciting poetry. Contest winners had rose petals strewn on them and received wreaths and rose bouquets. High priests released white doves into the air and showered water on the crowds to celebrate their survival of the Great Flood.

The word *Vartivar* has two meanings: "the flaming of the rose" and "to sprinkle with water." As recently as 100 years ago, to celebrate Vartivar, children in some villages would gather up branches, hide behind trees, and make a ruckus until their neighbors got fed up and came outside and tossed buckets of water on the children. Today the ritual has taken a slightly different form. During late July neighborhood hooligans creep up behind people of all ages out in public—especially nicely dressed ones—and drench them with water. During Vartivar, people may have to go home and change clothing four or five times a day, but the holiday ritual is an amusing way to keep cool in the hot summer weather.

Hadik

When a baby's first tooth begins to emerge, families like to celebrate Hadik. *Hadik* means "small grain," which is

Young Armenians prepare to splash their neighbors with water on Vartivar Day.

what the baby's tooth might look like at first. Families in Armenia continue to enjoy this ancient pagan rite, even though today it is practiced more out of tradition than actual belief. Hadik is said to reveal a child's future profession or destiny, which, according to pagan custom, had already been determined by the gods before the baby was born. On the celebration day all the relatives are invited to the family's home for a feast. Before they begin, foods such as grains, raisins, and nuts are spooned over the baby's head, which is covered by a veil. Then objects that represent professions, such as a pen for a writer or a hammer for a builder, are placed in a circle around the baby. When the veil is removed, the first object that the baby grabs is supposed to indicate the child's future path as he or she grows up.

Armenian Martyrs' Day

Every year on April 24, Armenians all over the world commemorate Armenian Martyrs' Day—the day on which they remember the victims of the 1915 genocide. In Armenia tens of thousands of people make a procession to Dzidzernagaberd, the "Fortress of the Swallows." This monument is named for a bird that always returns to its nest, even if its home has been destroyed. It is a symbol of the dream that one day Armenians will return to the homes they were forced to leave behind.

Dzidzernagaberd is located on a quiet summit overlooking the city of Yerevan. The location and striking appearance of the monument create a powerful feeling of sadness and solitude. On this day, people of all ages and professions gather at the monument to pay their respects to those who perished in this massive attempt to eliminate the Armenian people. Mourners line up to lay flowers at the "eternal flame" inside the fortress. The flame burns to represent the Armenian spirit, which can never be extinguished. The enormous panels of the fortress symbolize the different regions of Armenia that were attacked and occupied by the Turks. The tall, needle-shaped shaft beside it represents the rebirth of the Armenian people.

Armenians gather to pay their respects at the Martyrs' Monument.

Although April 24 is a day of sadness and mourning, Armenians also consider it a day of unity. Memorial gatherings all over the world serve to remind everyone that although the Armenians have suffered many dreadful episodes in the past, their nation has survived. For many Armenians the day represents a time to renew their commitment to gain Turkish recognition of the genocide and to restore their historic homeland.

Family Life, Hospitality, and Food

Armenia is a patriarchal society, a society in which males are recognized as the heads of families or clans. After the father the next person in charge of supporting a family is the firstborn son. But Armenian households are made up of more than parents and their children. Outside of the major cities, it is normal for many relatives, including grandparents, aunts, uncles, and cousins, to live under one roof as what is called an extended family. The eldest women on the father's side of the family are in charge of running the household. Although some people live only with their spouses and children, it is common practice for the bride to move in with her husband and his family. It is often said that once a new wife has her first child, she exercises more authority within the family.

In urban areas the average couple has two or three children. Families are larger, however, outside of the major cities. Although children everywhere help out with laundry chores and shopping errands, education for both boys and girls is encouraged. In rural areas boys often learn the family trade after high school. Girls are expected to prepare for marriage and motherhood by learning how to cook and care for children.

Brides are often taken to church in cars that have dolls attached to their front hoods.

Most Armenians marry early in life. There are good reasons for this. Until the recent development of modern medicines and vaccines, children did not always survive infancy. By marrying young, women had more years to bear children, and this raised the chances that a few would live. Outside of Yerevan, Armenians still cling to this tradition. It is normal for a girl of 16 to be married already and have a child. Although most couples today fall in love and choose to marry each other, there are still many arranged marriages, in which parents select their children's mates. If a boy is interested in a girl, however, and feels that her family will disapprove of the match, he might decide on *hars baghtzoo,* in which he kidnaps and elopes with the bride.

A typical family gathering around the dinner table

Armenian Hospitality

Cuisine plays an important role in Armenian culture. Offering food is a way to show respect and goodwill toward others. Anytime people come to visit, expected or unexpected, the hosts always offer them food or drink. Even if the guests are not particularly hungry, they must have something. Their hosts will insist. Guests should not appear too hungry, though. While it is a terrible offense for a guest to refuse to eat, it is not polite to accept an offer of food too eagerly either.

Foreign visitors are always amazed when Armenians they have barely met invite them over for a lavish dinner. Table settings are made to look pretty no matter what is being served. There might be fresh flowers or a bowl of candy as a centerpiece. The more elaborate the table setting, the more honored the guests should feel. Because the festivities can go on for quite a long time, there is no point in looking at your watch. "Armenian time" does not particularly follow schedules. Armenians love to experience their leisure time fully and refuse to have a clock tell them when it is time to end their merrymaking.

Whenever two or more people have a meal together, it is proper to make formal toasts. This ritual is taken very seriously. A toastmaster, called a *tamada* and usually a man, is selected. Typically he is very witty and has had plenty of experience making speeches. It is his job to say some touching words about the occasion that brought everyone together. The tamada may toast the hosts, national martyrs, parents and children, and Mount Ararat. Then the tamada "opens the floor" for toasts from other guests, who take turns saying something meaningful. A typical toast includes the words *Genatsut* or*Voghch leeness,* "to your health." Toasts are a beautiful tradition, but you must be careful to temper your intake, or you will have too much! To refuse to drink to someone's health is an insult to the person.

Armenians are generous in many ways and cherish the company of others. When making a new friend or meeting someone from abroad, a native likes to give the visitor a memento, or *hishadag,* to be remembered by. The memento might be a book, a jar of fruit preserves, or a photo of themselves.

Food, Glorious Food

Because historic Armenia lay at the crossroads of East and West, cuisines intermingled there as much as people did. Nearly every nation in the eastern Mediterranean area has at one time or another claimed certain dishes that are common throughout the region as its own. Some meals in eastern Armenia show hints of Russian influence with dishes such as *tarama salata,* a salty red caviar spread. Caviar, or clusters of fish eggs, is considered a delicacy in Armenia and in much of the world. An Armenian family named Petrossian has helped make caviar an international symbol of fine dining. Cuisine from historic Armenian regions includes many foods common in Greece, Syria, and Turkey. Some foods are called by their Turkish names, a reminder of the days when Armenia was a part of the Ottoman Empire, where Turkish was the official language.

Armenians like to cook with lots of greens, grains, and olive oil. Such foods are part of the "Mediterranean diet" that nutritionists say helps people live long, healthy lives.

Among Armenian cooks, meat, either lamb or pork, is highly prized and prepared in a variety of ways. Meat is often skewered for shish kebabs. The word *shish kebab* describes how cubes of meat are skewered and grilled over an open flame. Shish kebabs are most popularly prepared with tomatoes, eggplant, peppers, and onions that are roasted on skewers, too. The preferred way to prepare

A shish kebab vendor

lamb is *khorovats,* in which choice parts are barbecued on the bone. *Khashlama* is a country-style preparation, in which every section of the lamb is boiled in a stew. People traditionally soak up the tangy stew juices with bread or drink them.

One of the most basic and widely used food items in Armenia is bulgur, or cracked wheat kernels. Bulgur is cooked and served in mixed vegetable dishes as well as with meat or in soups. Another essential food in Armenian cuisine is *madzoon,* or yogurt. Madzoon has long been touted as the Armenians' secret to a long life. Not only do natives eat this ancient Armenian dairy product regularly, but many women use it as a skin cream on their faces at night.

Mealtime

A typical Armenian breakfast might include eggs scrambled with tomatoes and peppers; bread, cheese, honey, fruit jam, and tea. *Katah,* a sweet hard biscuit, is a favorite with hot beverages. Coffee breaks are typical in the afternoon. After drinking thick Armenian coffee in miniature cups, people flip them over so that the grounds on the bottom of the cup drip into the saucer. Fortunes are read from the patterns formed in the dried coffee grounds. This practice, called *bakht,* or *fahl* is a well-loved Armenian tradition.

Besides their thick coffee, Armenians like special drinks such as their own sweet mountain water and fruit nectars. Two distinctly Armenian drinks are bottled natural mineral water called *jermuk* and a refreshing yogurt and water mixture called *tahn.* Armenia is well-known for its award-winning brandies. These alcoholic after-dinner drinks are made from apricots, peaches, and other sweet fruits. Since the fall of the Soviet Union and the beginning of the

Women bake bread in a traditional oven called a tonir.

blockade of Armenia, however, production of Armenia's spectacular cognacs and wines has dropped. Armenians have other favorite beverages, though, including *oghi,* a transparent, licorice-flavored liqueur that turns cloudy when water is added. Vodka, another alcoholic beverage, is also popular at all times of day. Thirsty tourists find out too late that glasses of clear liquid placed before them at breakfast, lunch, or dinner contain not water but vodka.

Bread is an essential element of every Armenian meal. The national bread of Armenia is *lavash*, a thin, flat, chewy bread in which Armenians like to roll meat, cheese, or vegetables for sandwiches. For thousands of years lavash has been baked along the walls of a *tonir*, a barrel-shaped clay oven packed into the ground. A wood fire burns at the bottom of the tonir, heating its walls. Normally lavash is made by women who work in mills or workshops that have tonirs in them. The raw lavash dough is slapped against the walls of the tonir with a soft baking pad that looks like a small ironing board. The dough will stick to the wall and bake in a matter of minutes. Then it is carefully removed and laid out to cool before it is folded in halves or quarters. Tonirs are also used to provide central heating for rural families in the winter.

Armenian appetizers have a reputation for being so delicious that many people prefer them to the main course! Different kinds of breads are eaten with spreads or spicy meats such as *soujoukh.* Raw and cooked vegetables are made into salads and finger food. One favorite appetizer is *tutvash* or *tourshi*, which is pickled carrots, cabbage, green tomatoes, and other vegetables. Another favorite that is eaten at any meal is a soft, kneaded cheese called *tel banir.* Tel banir is pulled apart into strings like spaghetti.

One of the many mouth-watering dishes of Armenia is *dolma.* Dolma is a mixture of spiced and minced lamb and cooked rice pilaf stuffed into the skin of tomatoes, green peppers, or eggplants or rolled in grape or cabbage leaves like a cigar. *Herisseh* is a holiday porridge that combines shredded lamb or chicken, barley, and lots of butter.

At mealtime children are encouraged to eat every bite. In some households at the turn of the century, parents often cautioned their children not to leave scraps of food on their plates or their sweethearts would have scarred faces. If they licked their plates clean, their sweethearts would be handsome or beautiful—or so it is said.

Juicy watermelons, peaches, plums, pears, apples, cherries, and apricots are just as popular for dessert as rich pastries. *Bourma* and *pakhlava* are delicious pastries made of layers of baked, paper-thin filo dough. The pastries are either laid flat or rolled, are filled with walnuts, pistachios, or other nuts, and are covered with a honey syrup. Cakes are prepared for birthdays. *Halvah,* made from ground sesame seeds and molasses or honey, is also served on special occasions. And everyone who visits Armenia comments on how tasty the ice cream is.

In the United States an Armenian immigrant named George Mardikian introduced Armenian cuisine to American diners in the 1930s. He owned the famous Omar Khayyam restaurant in San Francisco. Celebrities such as the shah of Iran, First Lady Eleanor Roosevelt, actor Orson Welles, and heiress Barbara Hutton fell in love with the restaurant's exotic menu, which included rose-petal preserves. Always eager to express his gratitude to the United States for giving the Armenians a new home after the Turkish massacres, Chef Mardikian earned a reputation in the United States not only for his cooking talent, but for his generosity and goodwill. He was awarded the Medal of

Freedom for improving food service for U.S. troops fighting in Korea. He later won the Horatio Alger Award for showing young people that through hard work and kindness, anyone can realize a dream, no matter what his or her ethnic or religious background happens to be.

Recipes You Can Try at Home

Jajukh

This chilled cucumber and yogurt soup is cool and refreshing anytime.

2 medium cucumbers
1 quart plain yogurt
1 1/2 cups ice-cold water
1 clove garlic
1/4 teaspoon salt
1 tablespoon dry mint (optional)

1. Wash and peel the cucumbers. Cut lengthwise into quarters and then crosswise into quarter-inch slices.
2. Stir the yogurt in a bowl until smooth. Add the ice water and blend.
3. In a separate bowl, add salt to the garlic and crush. Then add to the yogurt mixture with the cucumbers and stir well. Add crushed mint if desired. Serve chilled. Makes 4 servings.

Khoshap

This dried fruit compote is an ancient dessert.

5 cups water
1/2 cup sugar
1 cup dried pitted prunes
1 cup dried apricots
1/2 cup dried pears
1/4 cup seedless golden raisins
1 stick cinnamon
2 tablespoons pine nuts

1. In a large saucepan, boil the water and sugar for 10 minutes. Stir until the sugar is dissolved.
2. Add the prunes and boil 5 minutes. Add the apricots, pears, raisins, and cinnamon stick. Lower the heat and simmer for 15 minutes or until the fruit is tender.
3. Remove from the heat and stir in the pine nuts. Cool to room temperature. Transfer to a deep serving bowl and remove the cinnamon stick. Cover and refrigerate until chilled. Makes 4 servings.

Paree Akhorjag! (Bon Appetit!)

Getting By in Armenia

Before independence the average number of cars per family in Armenia was among the highest of all Soviet republics. Today increasing automobile and fuel costs keep the roads from becoming too congested. With few exceptions, only men drive motor vehicles in Armenia. Most automobiles are imported from Russia. They include four-door sedans such as the Gaz and the Volga, two-door compact cars such as the Lada and the Moskovich, and three-door hatchbacks such as the Niva. The midsize Daewoo, from South Korea, is also popular. A small percentage of extremely wealthy people drive imported Mercedes-Benzes and BMWs.

For Armenians who do not own cars, buses, taxis, and subways are the most common forms of transportation. In major cities many buses run on electrical cables. People of all ages also ride bicycles to get around or just for fun. In rural areas a local bus usually operates at least once a day to take people to and from work, school, or shopping excursions. In villages some people ride on horseback. The blockade and other circumstances have closed borders and halted local and foreign travel by rail. To get in and out of the country, travelers might use Armenian

Repairing a bus cable

Airlines, The Iranian Caspian Airline Company, Russian or Romanian national airlines—which all provide regular international air service. There are also smaller airstrips, including Yerebouni and Shirak airports, for plane and helicopter travel.

Although the fuel shortage has slowed the pace of economic progress, it has also helped clear the air, as auto emissions created a great deal of pollution in most cities. Armenians find transportation problems frustrating but are never completely discouraged. They have always relied on the kindness of their fellow citizens to get by when they find themselves in tight situations. If you are lost or walking a great distance, many drivers with room to spare are very willing to lend a hand by picking you up.

Communication

Word of mouth is still the most common way that Armenians exchange the latest bits of information. Television and radio are more recent ways that people keep up with developing news. Television programs range from game shows and nature programs to Brazilian soap operas that have been dubbed in Russian.

The two types of radio outlets in Armenia include FM radio, which is operated domestically and heard all over the country, and shortwave, which broadcasts foreign programs over long distances. Young people especially like to listen to *Hye FM Radio,* which features lots of music from Europe and the United States. There are even programs operated by and for the Kurdish and Yezidi communities, broadcast in their native languages. *Radio Free Europe, Radio Liberty,* and *Voice of America* are widely listened to on shortwave radio. All three report international news from abroad. Families in very mountainous or earthquake-prone regions often do not have TV, radio, or telephone access.

Magazines and newspapers are read regularly, although they sometimes appear infrequently because of paper shortages and other economic obstacles. An English-language weekly newspaper called *Noyan Tapan* is read by foreigners who visit or work in Armenia. Since 1995 several newspapers that criticized government policies have been banned from operation. While observers such as the United Nations

Development Programme consider this a "serious setback for freedom of the press," many people hope that in this new age of democratic reform, the Armenian government will allow the publications to reopen and practice freedom of speech.

Anyone using the local telephone system must be ready to meet other people. Because telephone communication lines often crisscross, phone calls can turn into brief encounters with people you never intended to talk to. In addition, it is sometimes necessary to dial the same number three times before getting through. The first time may give a busy signal, the second time might connect you with a wrong number, and the third time you may hear someone else's telephone conversation on your line.

Government officials, large businesses, universities, and the media have access to all sorts of electronic devices, such as fax machines, cellular phones, and modems. These groups make up a small minority of the total population, however. Natives still agree that in both cities and villages, the best form of communication among ordinary people is face-to-face conversation.

Utilities

Armenians have learned to get by even when economic shortages affect every aspect of their lives. Candles and kerosene lamps are common in homes where regular electricity is unavailable. Every family has a supply of *speerts,* which look like mini-hockey pucks and burn like flares. Speerts are placed under free-standing grills and are used to heat water in teakettles and pans. People also submerge specially-made wire-bound heating units in pots and pans to boil water.

All over the country, tap water runs irregularly. Families often keep their water faucets in the open position over large containers in case they are sleeping when the water comes on. When that happens, everyone fills buckets or bathtubs with water to use throughout the day. While the water runs, people heat water on hot plates to bathe and wash laundry and dishes by hand. Although these arrangements are inconvenient and time-consuming, Armenians have grown used to working around them. While there are washing machines, dryers, and vacuum cleaners for sale in stores, they are expensive and require the kind of water volume and electricity that the authorities are not yet able to supply. Instead, most people wash clothes by hand, dry them on clotheslines, and sweep the floors and rugs with a broom.

Energy

Like many other former republics of the Soviet Union, Armenia has a power plant that runs on nuclear energy. Nuclear power plants were first built decades ago in

Soviet states that had no other way to generate electricity. When the Chernobyl nuclear disaster in Ukraine spread radiation all over the countryside, people began to take a second look at the efficiency level of other plants operating within the Soviet Union. After the 1988 earthquake Armenia's Medzamor nuclear power station was shut down. Environmental groups and energy experts felt that there were too many safety hazards at the plant. Medzamor might emit deadly radiation and is built on an earthquake fault line. However, with energy shortages and few other alternatives for power, the authorities have little choice but to reopen the plant. Today both Armenian and Russian specialists continue to conduct tests and attempt to modernize Medzamor.

Shopping

Because people must travel widely to get all the goods they need, shopping is an all-day affair. There are more specialty stores that sell baked goods or dairy products, for example, than there are central markets and department stores. Shopping also takes time because Armenians do a lot of browsing and comparing before they buy, and the selection and cost of products vary greatly from market to market. In addition, stores do not always receive expected goods or may sell out of them before some customers

At the marketplace

arrive. For major purchases it is best for families without cars to shop in groups. This way family members can carry all the bags home themselves.

For those who have never seen a bazaar, shopping in Armenia is a rare experience. Hundreds of vendors bring their home-grown fruits and vegetables to marketplaces and stack their produce in colorful displays. Every merchant has a scale to weigh produce for the customer. It is customary for shoppers to taste the food before buying it. And there are often no prices on items, as bargaining is an accepted practice.

People always carry bags with them, just in case they find an unexpected bargain or rare item for sale even when they are not specifically looking for something. In most areas, shopping bags are not free, and vendors do not accept checks or credit cards, although some stores have foreign exchange stations. Shop owners will not, however, exchange soiled or wrinkled American currency or bills dated before 1990. They believe that soiled currency is of lesser value, and dated bills might be counterfeit.

Before the breakup of the Soviet Union, shops called collectives, or cooperatives, were fully or partly run by the government. The Western idea of a free-market system is only a recent development. Today foreign-owned businesses are making their first-ever appearance in Armenia and the other former Soviet republics.

School Life

Armenian writer Petros Dourian once said, "School and press are the two pivots of our progress." He meant that the development of a people and a nation depend on the quality of their education and literature. This could not be more true. Armenians value education and consider it a priority. Armenia has the largest number of specialists with college degrees of all the CIS countries, and its literacy rate is 99 percent. As important as education may be, though, the government today does not have the funds to provide the country's schools with everything they need. And in many families, schooling and textbooks compete with other important needs such as food and clothing.

Children in Armenia begin attending school between the ages of five and seven. The educational system in Armenia provides many levels of learning, including preschools, elementary schools, junior and senior high schools, vocational and technical schools, and universities. There are even boarding schools for students who want to study in a city but live too far away to commute every day.

All over the nation old teaching methods and texts are being replaced with new approaches and books. Before independence the upper and middle classes in society were never mentioned. They were assumed not to exist. Now

It is customary to wear black and white to school.

that different social classes are freely acknowledged, new textbooks no longer refer to the population with terms such as "the working people of Armenia." While some aspects of Soviet instruction have been abandoned, some still remain.

Most classes are taught in Armenian, Russian, or both languages. There are also special schools that teach in English and French. Both are important languages to learn for young people who want to work in international business. Courses in math, science, and geography are also taught. Colleges such as Yerevan State University and the American University of Armenia offer classes that teach the English language. Some classes are even conducted in English.

At the end of each school year, each grade level marks the passing of examinations in a graduation ceremony. From kindergarten to high school, pupils celebrate the end of the year by performing folk dances and plays, singing songs, and reciting poetry. On the last day of school, graduates in Yerevan pour into Republic Square for an evening of fun and mischief. Many get rowdy and jump into the singing fountains fully dressed. This celebration is called *Verchi zangi gisher*, or Night of the Last Bell.

Options for Graduates

After graduating from junior high, young people can continue their academic education, go to a vocational or technical school, or get a full-time job. At a technical school students can expect on-the-job training in a factory as part of their education. Just as in the other former Soviet republics, there are also special schools for children who are especially gifted in athletics or the performing arts. In these schools, students can sharpen their unique talents and study academics at the same time.

During the Soviet period it was routine to encourage children to pursue a career in a field in which they showed special abilities, whether they wanted to enter that field or not. Since the breakup of the Soviet Union, however, a student's own preferences are taken into account. Because the economy is still developing in Armenia, though, students might be encouraged to enter a field in which they stand a better chance of finding a job. They might also major in a special subject because their families know people who may be able to find them a job in that area after they graduate.

Changes in Education

When Armenia became independent, educators and the new authorities realized that textbooks needed to be revised. Most were outdated, and others contained factual errors. In addition, all the written texts reflected Soviet policies. New textbooks have begun to be produced in Armenia. Without a central government like the one that supported the former republics in the past, however, there have been problems. Paper shortages and lack of state funding have made it difficult to publish and distribute the number of books that are needed.

In addition, it has been a challenge to find ways to maintain and repair school property when needed construction materials have been held up or confiscated at Armenia's borders. Teachers, parents, and Armenian charities in the diaspora have donated chalkboards, classroom furniture, heaters, and school supplies. When it comes to lessons, everyone is expected to improvise and share. This means that parents may lend books to teachers to lecture from or students and instructors may bring newspaper articles from home to discuss in class.

While the Armenians have always prized education, the recent energy crisis and the transition to independent statehood have had a profound effect on the school system in Armenia. More private schools have opened up since Armenia became independent. Although many families cannot afford to enroll their children, these schools provide a high level of education to bright and eager students who can attend them. The energy crisis has halted classroom study in many public schools during the colder months, when adequate heating cannot be guaranteed. Classes are often interrupted by long winter recesses. Many parents would like to be able to afford the annual tuition to send their children to other schools. Parents who can afford to pay send their children to private schools or spend up to $1,000 per course for special tutoring in which teachers offer one-on-one instruction.

The shift to independent statehood has brought other unexpected changes to school life in Armenia. Some schools are in session for a half day. Others divide the school day into two shifts. This must be done because there are more students than there are teachers and adequate classrooms. When new economic policies went into effect, many teachers left the profession because they could not

Many young boys are skipping college to become street vendors in order to support their families' immediate needs.

manage to live on the salaries paid. Currently more than 75 percent of the teachers in Armenia are women. Men, traditionally the chief wage earners in their households, need to earn larger salaries and cannot afford to work in the teaching field at this time. The temporary half-day arrangement allows today's teachers to take on other jobs that can supplement their salaries. Half days also allow children to help their parents operate the family business or take care of household chores while their parents are working. Both students and teachers find it difficult to pay for rising public bus and subway fares to get to school. While the present government is trying to find ways to improve the quality of life since Soviet days, it is taking time for citizens to see real improvements.

Another serious development in education in Armenia today is that many children do not feel encouraged to pursue a college education. Upon graduation many young people find that there are few careers in their chosen fields that can support them and their future families. Both parents and teachers are doing their best to show children the importance of education despite all of these hardships. This issue is of great concern to Armenians, who say that for the first time the next generation runs the risk of being less educated than their parents.

Sports and Recreation

Like education, athletic activity is strongly encouraged in Armenia. Some favorite outdoor sports include soccer, skiing, tennis, and track and field. Indoor sports such as boxing, weight lifting, gymnastics, and swimming are also very popular. Over the past decade interest in self-defense sports such as karate and judo has grown, too.

Armenians are avid soccer fans. They call soccer *football.* Soccer is the national sport of Armenia. It is played in gymnasiums, streets, fields, and just about anywhere else where a little legroom is found. There are local teams in nearly every region of Armenia. Major games are played in Armenia's Hrazdan Stadium, which seats 75,000 spectators. In the 1970s the national team, called Ararat, won several Soviet Cup championships. In those days fans wore Ararat T-shirts and plastered bumper stickers everywhere. The national team has since joined the European Union Football Association. Now that the old Soviet football associations no longer exist, it is hoped that membership in the European organization will help reestablish training camps and soccer clubs for young athletes.

Skiing is another sport that Armenians enjoy. The most popular slopes are at Tsaghgatsor, which was a premiere

Major soccer games are played in Yerevan's Hrazdan Stadium.

training ground for all Soviet Olympic skiers. Armenia also has many outdoor courts for tennis and handball. In the field of tennis, one of the most popular names in Armenian circles is Sargis Sargsian. This young man moved from Yerevan to the United States to study at Arizona State University. While in Armenia, Sargsian had few opportunities to participate in competitions following the breakup of the Soviet Union. In the United States he had more chances to play in tournaments. The move to the United States has definitely paid off for Sargsian. Since moving he has won four Grand Slam singles titles in the National Collegiate Athletic Association (NCAA).

All over Armenia young sports enthusiasts like to read

weekly newspapers and magazines devoted to sports. Some favorites include *Football Plus, Marzagan Hayasdan* (Sports of Armenia), and *Marzashkhar* (The World of Sports).

Games People Play

Besides strenuous sports such as soccer and tennis, Armenians love games that require mental concentration, such as backgammon and chess. Armenians enjoy the skill involved in playing a board game like backgammon, but they also enjoy the element of chance provided by the roll of the dice. It is not unusual for excitable backgammon players to smack their game pieces down on the board in a noisy fashion. Backgammon boards can be works of art. Carpenters make special sets using different colors of natural wood, which are varnished and inlaid in the board. Backgammon tournaments at the local and national levels lead to championships that pit players from all over the Caucasus region against each other.

Did you know that the word chess players use when they beat their opponents—*checkmate*—comes from the Armenian word for chess, *shakhmat?* (In Persian it means "the shah is dead.") People take chess playing quite seriously in Armenia. They are very proud that the undisputed chess champion of the world—Garry Kasparov—is part Armenian. At the age of 22, Kasparov became the

World chess champ Garry Kasparov

youngest world champion in the history of chess. When he beat longtime world champion Anatoly Karpov in 1985, he became the highest-rated chess player in the world. Kasparov was born in Baku, Azerbaijan, in 1963. He and his family fled the city when persecution and massacres forced Armenians out in 1990. Kasparov challenged the old, corrupt Soviet Chess Federation and went on to set up the Grandmasters' Association, which is made up of the most talented chess players in the world, and a series of international chess tournaments called the World Cup.

Kasparov says that a good memory is one of the most important qualities a chess player can have. He commits every move he and others have made in their chess careers to memory. When the German magazine *Der Spiegel* showed him five chess positions and asked him to tell them what matches they were from, he identified who played in the matches and remembered the year and place besides. Today he tests his skill and endurance by spending hours studying and practicing his moves.

The Olympics

Preparing for the Olympics is another great test of endurance. Training regimens are strict, and the hours of practice are long. Olympic hopefuls know that to be the best at anything takes a lot of discipline and training. In Soviet days, if a boy or girl showed a special ability in gymnastics, for example, the child was encouraged to begin training for the Olympics as early as the first few years in elementary school. In those days the state would sponsor all athletes training for the Olympics, paying for their coaches, instruction, uniforms, and transportation and providing salaries for them, too. Many special privileges were also given to Olympic athletes. Athletes and their families often skipped ahead of others who were waiting for available apartments, for instance.

From 1952 to 1988, Armenian athletes competed on the Soviet Olympic team. In that time Armenians won 18 gold, 9 silver, and 7 bronze medals for the USSR. In the Olympic games Armenian athletes have performed especially well in gymnastics, weight lifting, wrestling, boxing, and diving. Israel Melitosian, Yuri Sargsian, and Yuri Vardanian are three famous Armenian weight lifters who earned gold medals at numerous Olympiads. When Israel Melitosian won another gold medal at the Summer Olympics held in Barcelona in 1992, he felt very proud to represent his Armenian homeland and hear his own national anthem played in honor of his victory. At the same time he was very sad that his brother, sister, and fellow Armenians who had died in the recent earthquake were not alive to share his happiness with him.

During the Soviet regime the most talented athletes from all of the 15 republics had to engage in rigorous competitions to win the honor of representing the USSR at the Olympics. Competition was fierce among the republics. Armenians claimed that they had to be twice as good as Russian competitors to be selected by the judges, because Russian athletes were often favored by the central Soviet authorities.

Nowadays the newly independent states are struggling to develop their own national teams without the financial support they once had from Soviet authorities. Sending

Olympic gold medalist Israel Melitosian

a team to the Olympics is an expensive venture, and it is still a new concept for the Armenian team to participate as an independent nation. Transportation, equipment, and coaches all cost money. Although the Armenian government is fully supporting the Armenian Olympic team, the team also receives added assistance it greatly needs. Fund-raising efforts by Armenians in the United States and other countries help cover housing, meals, and other essentials for the athletes. The athletes' backers also want to encourage athletes to remain in their chosen fields by supporting them financially. Therefore, fund-raising committees also collect prize money to be awarded at other events so that the athletes can make a living in their fields.

As a nation Armenia looks forward to placing its own athletic achievements on the Olympic map. The republic's success at future Olympiads will depend, however, not only on how skilled and talented its athletes are, but on how successful the authorities are in raising financial support for the competitors.

Recreation for All

During the hot summers children in Armenia do not make wishes and throw coins into one of Yerevan's many decorative public fountains. The boys swim in them! On hot afternoons swarms of boys in briefs horse around in the shallow pools and spray everyone around them. Girls and adults cannot cool down this way, though. Fountain swimming for girls and anyone who does not look like a preteen is frowned upon.

After school and at recess time, elementary-school children enjoy games such as bombardment, called *kordzakordz*, and hide-and-seek. Boys like to play buck-buck, known as *eshek* or *esh militzia*, in which as many as possible from one team vault onto the backs of players from the opposite team. Typical games for young girls include hopscotch and cat's cradle. Girls also love to pick wildflowers for their teachers or for table settings at home.

Taking a dip in one of Yerevan's fountains

Children all over Armenia are very inventive about games, especially when there are few store-bought toys to be found. They might play with household items such as sifters, or build go-carts out of found objects, or play jacks with tiny lamb knucklebones! Some women also tell fortunes with the bones. Although games vary from district to district, one thing remains the same: Children play outside whenever the weather permits.

Wherever they are, Armenians seek rest and relaxation in the great outdoors, appreciating the beauty of nature. There are public picnic grounds along almost every scenic drive and babbling stream in Armenia. These picnic sites typically have a small, decorated fountain from which mountain spring water flows.

These recreation spots, tucked away in the mountains, are beautiful places to take a rest during a long excursion. They are also great destinations in themselves. Families and friends might stop for lunch, take a hike or swim, or just sit back and relax with the family and a few watermelons.

Road travel in Armenia brings many wonderful surprises. The roads are not cluttered with route signs or notices to indicate that a restaurant is five miles ahead. Armenians operate very well without road signs, maps, or landmarks. Even those who are not seasoned navigators are good at getting around.

In addition to public recreation facilities, Armenia also has spas and health resorts in picturesque areas. One such

The shores of Lake Sevan

resort is the Lake Sevan National Park, Nature Reserve, and Resort. The scenery around the lake is so breathtaking and the water of the lake itself so blue that people call it the blue-eyed beauty of Armenia. In fact, one famous writer declared, "Sevan is so beautiful you want to drown in it!" That definitely was not the case when Ygor Nersisyan entered the Guinness Book of World Records for swimming the width of Lake Sevan in 1990. This long-distance swimmer swam across the lake in 15 hours, 59 minutes, and 37 seconds. Lake Sevan is 28 miles (45 kilometers) wide.

Besides swimming, vacationers at Lake Sevan can enjoy watersports such as motorboating, sailing, and waterskiing. Since the ishkhanatzook is becoming an endangered species, fishing enthusiasts must apply for special permits so that the authorities can guard against poaching. The Sevan area has historic monuments, summer homes, hotels, restaurants, camps, a writer's colony, and even a sports complex. Other resort spots, in Tsaghkatzor, Dilijan, Jermuk, and Piurakan, also attract visitors year-round. They offer activities such as skiing and mineral-bath treatments, which have been praised for their medicinal value.

These resorts, as well as summer camps, are now all privately owned. Unfortunately only a fraction of Armenia's vacation spots and camps are open today, however, because the demand for them has decreased and some still house homeless earthquake victims and Armenian refugees from Azerbaijan. Not all families can afford to go to a resort or send their children to camp. In Soviet days the camps used to be free of charge.

Children can enjoy two recreational centers for youth in Yerevan: the Youth Palace and the Children's Museum of Armenia. The Youth Palace is dedicated solely to young people. Inside the center is a hotel, a movie and concert hall, a gymnasium, and a disco. There is even a revolving restaurant on the roof. Established in 1970, the Children's Museum of Armenia was the first major museum of children's art in the world. The museum houses more than 150,000 works by children from more than 100 countries. Visits to the museum offer young people a unique opportunity to get to know children from all over the world through the subjects they paint.

Young people in Armenia also enjoy clubs. The country's youth-oriented organizations include Youth for Armenia. This teen club introduces American culture and lifestyles to young people. The club has also held round table discussions between youth of Armenia, Georgia, and Azerbaijan to address social and economic issues that affect them all. A special youth organization called Pyunic, or "Phoenix," gives children with physical handicaps renewed confidence through sports activities and competitions. Pyunic also helps arrange summer-camp sponsorships and participation in the Special Olympics.

Armenians in the United States

Unlike people of most nationalities, more Armenians live outside their homeland than within it. Why is this so? Over the years some Armenians made their living as traveling merchants, in countries as diverse as Poland, India, and Ethiopia. Many also fled their homeland to avoid discrimination. Others were driven out. The largest wave of Armenian immigration to the United States and other countries took place during the Armenian genocide. People began to flee as early as 1895, when it became clear that Turkish policies would not provide safety for Armenians. The United States was known as a safe haven where people could practice their own beliefs and customs and pursue their livelihoods in freedom. American missionaries and schoolteachers working in the Ottoman Empire at the time encouraged Armenians to go to the United States. Those who survived the genocide escaped to any country that would take them in. Today there are Armenian communities on almost every continent on Earth, and in nations as distant and as different as Australia, Israel, and Switzerland.

Making a New Life

Having narrowly escaped death and carrying only bare

essentials, most Armenian exiles started their new lives with no money or belongings. Armenians often took up work they knew from home, such as farming, rug dealing, weaving, and embroidery. Hagop Seropian and his family were the first of thousands of Armenians to move to Fresno, California. It is easy to understand why the farmland around Fresno appealed to Armenians. Many had heard their grandparents boast about the fertile land in Armenia, and how they could not hold one watermelon even with two hands. Farmers in Fresno had a reputation for growing egg-sized grapes and nine to ten pound eggplants! Today about 40,000 Armenians live in Fresno County, California, where their family-owned businesses continue to pack dried fruits and nuts and grow their own special varieties of melons, grapes, and raisins.

Once they arrived in the United States, Armenian refugees worked hard, saved their money, and began to rebuild their lives. Many sent ship-passage money to their relatives still in danger overseas. In the 1920s, Armenians still planned to return to their homes if and when the conditions in Turkey improved. However, Turkey's policy toward the Armenians did not change. And when Armenia became part of the Soviet Union, the idea of moving to a Communist country did not appeal to most Armenian Americans who treasured their newfound liberties in the United States. Armenians in the diaspora began to build churches and community centers in their new homes to maintain their

An Armenian refugee weaving a carpet

Armenian identity. They recognized that they would not be returning to Armenia in the near future.

Living in Two Worlds

As the children of Armenian immigrants began to go to public schools and take part in American life, they tried very hard to blend in with their American friends. To fit in, they gave up traditions that would brand them as different. Armenian boys named Arshavir began to call themselves Archie and refused to speak Armenian in public so that they would not be mocked by their friends. These efforts to Americanize, or become American, helped Armenians adapt to new lifestyles and values in the United States but also disconnected them from their Armenian heritage. Armenians faced a problem they had never before faced. For the first time, some Armenians did not speak the language of their ancestors and were marrying non-Armenians.

During the 1930s the Soviet leader Josef Stalin enforced a policy to suppress ethnic diversity within the Soviet republics, including Armenia. With the genocide still fresh in their memories, even the most hopeful of Armenians in the United States became concerned. They worried that Talaat Pasha's dream to exterminate all but one Armenian to exhibit in a museum might one day come true. Many felt that their small race would become extinct unless they could preserve their ethnic identity. Those who lived outside Armenia were gradually beginning to forget their old customs and ties to "the old country." Armenians called the process of slowly losing their connections to their homeland the White Genocide, because it was a nonviolent process through which their identity would eventually be wiped out. Today many Armenian Americans try to remember and practice the customs of their ancestors at the same time that they absorb everything they like about American culture. They are trying hard to be patriotic and productive members of two communities that are equally important to them.

Continual Immigrants

As time has passed, the Armenian community in the United States has developed many personalities. Many Armenians of different backgrounds continue to immigrate to the United States. Each new group goes through the process of adapting to a new land and learning the ins and outs of life in the United States. The civil war in Lebanon and the revolution in Iran in the 1970s were two events that uprooted Armenians once again and brought them to new countries. As minority groups continue to face restrictions in Turkey, a steady stream of Armenian immigrants continues to arrive in the United States. The difficult living conditions in independent Armenia have brought more Armenians to California, whose mountains and dry climate remind them of home. These new immigrants have added a new dimension to established Armenian communities in the United States. Armenians with different attitudes and lifestyles have had to learn how to get along with each other.

The Armenian Community

Today there are approximately four million Armenians in the Armenian diaspora. Of that number about 1 million live in the United States, where the majority make up a very prosperous segment of society. The largest community of Armenians in the United States today is located in southern California, where in the city of Glendale alone there are some 45,000 Armenians. In this region you can see Armenian-owned businesses with storefront signs written in both English and Armenian. The second largest, and one of the oldest Armenian communities in the United States, is in the New York metropolitan area, where 80,000 to 100,000 Armenians make their home. Many Armenian organizations also have their national headquarters in the New York area. The third largest community is in the greater Boston area, where about 50,000 Armenians live. Watertown, Massachusetts, is home to many

Armenian institutions, including the Armenian Library and Museum of America, which houses many artifacts and family heirlooms such as coins, rugs, and costumes.

The Armenian church is at the center of Armenian life and plays more than a religious role in people's lives. While many Armenian Americans attend church, many others have chosen to be active in other types of community organizations that have developed alongside church activities. Various youth groups run educational, cultural, social, and athletic programs for young Armenian Americans. In the United States, there are more than seven Armenian summer camps, hundreds of Armenian private schools, and many other organizations, which include social clubs, educational and cultural associations, charitable and humanitarian groups, and patriotic organizations.

The majority of Armenians follow the Armenian Apostolic faith. Although there are more than 100 Armenian Apostolic churches in the United States, they are not all under the jurisdiction of a single administration. When Armenia became a Soviet state, the Soviet authorities discouraged the practice of religion. Among other things this meant that only 20 churches at a time were allowed to operate in the entire nation. Many Armenian Americans who felt that Armenia should be a free and independent nation were not pleased that the church in Armenia had to answer to the Soviet government. Differences among

Catholicos Karekin I blessing holy oil in Armenia

Armenian Americans led to the establishment of two separate administrative church bodies with two spiritual leaders. Although the religious principles of the two churches were exactly the same, political views divided them. The split in the church led to the duplication of many Armenian church organizations. With the collapse of the Soviet Union, however, reunification of the two church bodies appears to be on the horizon.

Political Activities

Despite their humble beginnings, a large percentage of the children and grandchildren of immigrant Armenians are financially secure today, and the majority are college-educated professionals. In a country such as the United States, where people are encouraged to get involved in public affairs, Armenians have been active participants in the political system. Armenians even have lobbying groups that present Armenian interests to members of Congress. Two of the most important goals of these lobbying groups are to obtain humanitarian aid for Armenia and to have Congress pass a resolution calling for the commemoration of the Armenian genocide.

In recent years the government of Turkey has been putting political and economic pressure on U.S. officials to defeat this resolution. This has made Armenians around the world even more upset about what happened to their people more than 80 years ago. Armenians everywhere are deeply concerned about efforts to revise history, and Armenian groups in the diaspora continue to urge Turkey to admit to what was done. Armenians feel that this is the only way that the "open wounds" of the Armenian people will heal. It would be a first step toward cooperation between the neighboring countries of Armenia and Turkey.

Contributions of Armenian Americans

Armenian Americans have distinguished themselves in many fields including the arts, sciences, sports, and business. Billionaire businessman Kirk Kerkorian is considered one of the wealthiest people in the United States today. He has owned such companies as MGM movie studios and the massive hotel, casino, and theme park known as the MGM Grand. A son of immigrants from historic Armenia, Kerkorian earned a living for a short time as bouncer in a bowling alley and as a boxer nicknamed Rifle Right Kerkorian. Eventually he became a financier, and his confidence and aggressive business skills are famous in America's corporate boardrooms. Kerkorian is very modest about his success, however. His Lincy Foundation has made charitable contributions to many worthy causes, including the Red Cross, Boys and Girls Clubs, and aid to

Armenian Americans commemorating the Armenian genocide

Armenia. Most of his life Kerkorian has sought to avoid the spotlight. He has made donations to charities only on the condition that his gifts be anonymous.

Whenever you spend money, you are using a product that an Armenian American helped produce. A veterinarian and student of pharmacy, Kristapor Seropian created the black and green dyes used to print U. S. currency. In the late 1800s this immigrant from the Ottoman Empire was paid $6,000—a small fortune in those days—for the formula for his dye. Seropian went on to become a physician. Armenian Americans have applied their creative genius to other products as well, including Gatorade sports beverage, Mounds and Almond Joy candy bars, Colombo yogurt, and Zildjian cymbals.

The Academy Award-winning actress and singer Cher

was born Cherilyn Sarkissian. She has performed in movies such as *Mask, Mermaids, Moonstruck,* and *Suspect.* Following the 1988 earthquake, Cher responded to an appeal for help from a family who survived the tragedy. Moved by the suffering following the disaster, she visited the country of her ancestors for the first time to show her concern and support for fellow Armenians.

Hollywood director Rouben Mamoulian was another well-known Armenian American in the arts. He directed the first feature film using the colorizing process known as Technicolor. The film was *Becky Sharp*. Mamoulian also directed *The Mark of Zorro* and *Dr. Jekyll and Mr. Hyde.*

Another Armenian American, George Deukmejian, was governor of California during the 1980s and 1990s. Before that he had been a California state senator. Deukmejian is credited with many achievements as governor of the Golden State. His administration created 3 million new jobs, improved the quality of education in California schools, and upgraded the condition of the California highway system. Deukmejian says that the three most important principles his parents taught him were to know the value of a good education, to be honest with himself and with others, and to work hard to achieve his goals. He feels that in his career and personal life, their advice has served him well.

The Statue of Liberty, in New York Harbor, has extended her hand to people of every race and creed who

Cher lighting a candle in memory of the Armenian earthquake victims during her visit to Armenia

wanted a better life in the United States. Immigrants have made the United States the most ethnically diverse nation in the world. The special mix of people in the United States gives all Americans the unusual opportunity to learn first-hand about different customs and practices from around the globe. It also teaches them to be tolerant of those who are different. Armenian Americans are grateful to the U.S. government for giving them the chance to start their lives anew. They are also proud to make their own unique contributions to the multicultural society that America has been able to create.

Looking Toward the Future

Throughout history Armenians have faced many obstacles. Dealing with constant change and hardship from century to century has made them very flexible and adaptable. Dealing with oppression, persecution, and disappointment, however, has made them weary and doubtful. Now that Armenia is once again independent, Armenians continue to cope with new, surprising developments. All over again, the people are moving with caution as they adapt to new lifestyles and the influence of neighboring countries. Armenia is reestablishing itself as the land at the crossroads of East and West. Armenia's unique location will open the country to many influences from the rest of the world. Armenians are doing their best both to take advantage of new opportunities that can reshape and recreate their lives and to preserve traditions that are part of their national identity.

Today all of the former Soviet republics are struggling to make their new political systems work. Life was very different in the Communist state. There were many restrictions, but people could rely on certain routines and standards, such as weekly food shipments or free medical services. Today there is greater freedom, but routines and

Children hold the key to Armenia's future.

standards have changed. Services are not always reliable, and although more goods flow into the country than ever before, people are less able to afford them. Armenia's authorities have no plans to return to communism, but their long-term democratic goals cannot be achieved overnight. Today Armenians are coming to terms with the fact that making democracy work means participation. They cannot just let the government do everything the way it did during Communist times. People are learning that independence is a responsibility, not just a gift.

Many issues need to be worked through before the country can grow. Armenia will not begin to recover fully from recent natural disasters and develop as an independent state until the energy crisis is solved and the blockade surrounding Armenia comes to an end. Serious decisions about health and environmental issues will have to be made, and Armenia and her neighbors will have to take a stand on the rights of people in Nagorno Karabagh. The Armenian people bear the burdens of these times and look to the future, continuing to find strength and inspiration in their families, communities, and national traditions.

As Armenians in the diaspora continue to build bridges with their homeland, many hope one day to participate in day-to-day developments in Armenia as dual citizens. In addition, many Armenians in the United States have pledged to honor their past by keeping memories of the past alive in the present. Plans to build a Genocide Memorial Museum and a Genocide Research Institute have been drafted.

Armenians have grown to feel that throughout history their people have been like trees crushed by bulldozers. Armenians hold that though the bulldozers did their damage, they were not able to destroy their roots. From those roots a nation of Armenians has grown back time and again. Armenians liken themselves to the phoenix, the legendary bird that is consumed by fire only to rise from its own ashes. The Armenians too have emerged from ashes on many occasions. Today they are proud of their historic accomplishments and their new independence. Armenians live with hope and determination for the day when their horizon will be even brighter.

A piece of prose by the author William Saroyan is often recited by Armenian Americans. As they continue to survive and prosper outside of their historic homeland, Saroyan's words remind them of their past and comfort them when they think about their future.

> *I should like to see any power of the world destroy this race, this small tribe of unimportant people, whose wars have all been fought and lost, whose structures have crumbled, literature is unread, music is unheard, and prayers are no more answered. Go ahead, destroy Armenia. See if you can do it. Send them into the desert without bread and water. Burn their homes and churches. Then see if they will not laugh, sing and pray again. For when two of them meet anywhere in the world, see if they will not create a new Armenia.*
>
> —William Saroyan

Appendix A

The Armenian Language

Armenian belongs to what is called the Indo-European family of languages. Coincidentally there are 38 letters in the Armenian alphabet, and the Armenian language ranks thirty-eighth among the world's most frequently spoken languages.

The Armenian words used in this book contain many variations in spelling and pronunciation. Dialects spoken in present-day Armenia are not necessarily the same ones spoken by Armenians from the diaspora—whose family origins trace back to parts of what is now historic Armenia. Although the two major Armenian dialects vary in vocabulary and pronunciation, a person speaking Eastern Armenian can be understood by someone speaking Western Armenian, and vice versa.

Some Armenian Phrases

English	**Armenian**	**Armenian Script**
hello	barev	բարեւ
goodbye	tsuhdesootyoon	ցտեսութիւն
How are you?	Eench bes es? *or* Vonts es?	ինչ պէս՞ ես; ոնց՞ ես
I'm fine.	Lav em.	լաւ եմ
good morning	bari looys	բարի լոյս
good night	bari gisher	բարի գիշեր
please	hajis *or* khuntrem	հաճիս ; խնդրեմ
thank you	shunorhagalootyoon	շնորհակալութիւն
yes	ayo	այո
no	voch *or* cheh	ոչ ; չէ

APPENDIX B

Embassies, Consulates, and Missions of the Republic of Armenia in the United States and Canada

The Embassy of the Republic of Armenia
2225 R St., NW
Washington, D.C. 20008
Phone: (202) 319-1976
Fax: (202) 319- 2982

The Embassy of the Republic of Armenia
130 Albert St., Suite 1006
Ottawa, Ontario
K1P-5G4 Canada
Phone: (613) 234-3710
Fax: (613) 234-3444

Consulate General of the Republic of Armenia
50 N. La Cienega Blvd., Suite 210
Beverly Hills, CA 90211
Phone: (310) 657-6102
Fax: (310) 657-7419

Permanent Mission of the Republic of
Armenia to the United Nations
119 E. 36th St.
New York, NY 10016
Phone: (212) 686-9079
Fax: (212) 686-3934
E-mail address: ArmMission@mcimail.com

Glossary

achk (ahchk)—glass bead worn to ward off the evil eye

Anahit (AH nah heet)—goddess of fertility and wisdom worshiped by pagan Armenians

bakht or **fahl** (bahkt) or (fahl)—tradition of reading fortunes from coffee grounds

basdegh (BAHS degh)—sweet snack made from walnuts, molasses, and honey

Catholicos (KAH toh lih kohs)—spiritual leader of the Armenian Apostolic Church

diaspora (dye AS puh ruh)—group of people living outside of their homeland

dolma (DOHL mah)—grape leaves or other vegetables stuffed with lamb and rice

dram (DUH rahm)—Armenian unit of currency

duduk (DOO dook)—Armenian wind instrument that makes a haunting sound

dumbek and **dahol** (DOOM bek) and (DAH hohl)—types of Armenian drums

Dzidzernagaberd (dzee dzer nag a BERD)—name of the genocide monument in Yerevan, meaning "Fortress of the Swallows"

eshek or **esh militzia** (esh EK) or (esh mee lee TZYAH)—game of buck-buck

Etchmiadzin (ech mee ah DZEEN) **Cathedral**—oldest Christian church in Armenia

Geghard (GE ghard) **Monastery**—Armenian cave monastery
genocide (JEN uh syd)—organized plan to destroy an entire nationality or ethnic group
glasnost (GLAHS nust)—Russian word for "openness"
Grapar (GUR ah par)—classical form of Armenian
Gyumri (GYOOM ree)—second largest city in Armenia
Hadik (HAH deek)—celebration held when a baby's first tooth emerges
Haik Nahapet (hyk NAH hah pet)—legendary founding father of Armenia
Hayasdan (hye ahs DAHN)—Armenian word for Armenia
hekyat (HE kyat)—fable
herisseh (HE ree se)—porridge served on holidays
hishadag (HEE shah dahg)—memento or souvenir
ishkhanatzook (eesh khan ah TSOOK)—species of trout that exists only in Lake Sevan
jermuk (JER mook)—region with mineral hot springs, or mineral water
kanun (KAH noon)—an Armenian zither
katah (KAH tah)—sweet biscuit
kef (kef)—celebration or party
kemenchè (ke men CHE)—string instrument
khashlama (KHASH lah mah)—lamb stew
khatchkar (KHACH kar)—cross stone
khorovats (KHOH roh vahts)—barbecued lamb chops
Khor Virap (khor VEE rahp) **Monastery**—site where King Trdat imprisoned Saint Gregory for 14 years

Komitas Vardapet (KOH mee tahs VAHR dah pet)—monk who documented Armenian folk music for the first time
lavash (LAH vahsh)—Armenian flat bread
madagh (MAH dahgh)—traditional lamb sacrifice
madzoon (MAH dzoon)—yogurt
Matenadaran (mah te NAH dah rahn)—largest library of Armenian books and manuscripts in the world
Mer Hairenik (mer hye re NEEK)—"Our Fatherland," the Armenian national anthem
Mount Aragats (AH rah gahdz)—tallest mountain in Armenia
nakharar (NAH khah rahr)—Armenian prince and landowner in ancient and medieval times
oghi (AW ghee)—a clear, licorice-flavored liqueur that turns cloudy when water is added
perestroika (pe ruh STROI kuh)—Russian word for "rebuilding"
Sardarapat (SAHR dah rah pat)—monument built on a battle site in Armenia
shakhmat (shahkh MAHT)—chess
tahn (tahn)—yogurt drink
tamada (TAH mah dah)—toastmaster
tayyagvorti (tay yag vor TEE)—noble hostage
tel banir (TEL bah neer)—Armenian string cheese
tonir (TOH neer)—clay, barrellike oven dug into the ground in which lavash is baked
tuf (toof)—volcanic stone of Armenia
tutvash or **tourshi** (TUT vahsh) or (TOOR shee)—pickled vegetable appetizer

Vanadzor (VAH nah dzor)—third largest city in Armenia

Vardanantz (VAR dah nants)—day that Armenians celebrate their defense of Christianity

Vardan Mamikonian (var TAHN mah mee GOHN yan)—Armenian general who died at the battle of Avarayr to preserve Christianity

Vartivar (var TEE var)—celebration in which children drench people with water

vishap (VEE shahp)—legendary sea monster

white genocide—the absorption of a minority group into a larger cultural group

Yerebouni (YE re boo nee)—ancient name for Yerevan

Yerevan (YE re vahn)—capital city of Armenia

Zoroastrianism (zor oh AS tree uhn ihz um)—fire-worshiping religion

Selected Bibliography

Ananikyan, Rem. *Yerevan—A Guide.* Moscow: Progress Publishers, 1982.

Armenian International Magazine. Glendale, CA.

Avagian, Grigor. *Armenia and Armenians in the World.* Yerevan: Lensay/Omega-N Enterprises, 1994.

Avakian, Arra. *The Armenians in America.* Minneapolis: Lerner Publications, 1977.

Baliozian, Ara. *The Armenians: Their History and Culture.* New York: Ararat Press, 1980.

Bedrosian, Robert. *Armenia in Ancient and Medieval Times.* New York: Armenian National Education Committee, 1985.

Bournoutian, George. *A History of the Armenian People.* Vols. 1 and 2. Costa Mesa, CA: Mazda Publishers, 1995.

Engholm, Chris. *The Armenian Earthquake.* San Diego: Lucent Books, 1989.

Human Development Report for Armenia. Yerevan: The United Nations Development Programme, 1995.

Pellerier, Andre. *An Animated History of Armenia.* Glendale, CA: ALCO Printing, 1985.

Zeitlian, Garine. *The Armenian Genocide Handbook for Students and Teachers.* Glendale, CA: Armenian National Committee, W. Region, 1988.

INDEX

About the Author

Lucine Kasbarian is a descendant of survivors of the 1915 genocide of the Armenians, which drove her grandparents from their ancestral lands in historic Armenia, now within the borders of Turkey. A proud American, Ms. Kasbarian is grateful to the United States for offering her refugee ancestors a new home where they could pursue their dreams of freedom. She is also grateful to a dedicated Armenian community in the United States for encouraging her to preserve a precious cultural legacy. In this book she makes use of her knowledge of Armenian history and culture, gained from her parents, her studies, and her trips to Armenia—under both Soviet and independent rule.

Ms. Kasbarian, whose first name means "moon" in Armenian, has written for several publications in various roles, ranging from restaurant reviewer to United Nations correspondent. She volunteers her services to educational and cultural societies, including the Armenian Youth Federation and the Land & Culture Organization. It is her greatest wish that one day Armenians scattered all over the world who desire to do so will be able to return to their ancestral lands. The author lives in Teaneck, New Jersey.